THE ELEMENTAL BODY

THE ELEMENTAL BODY

A Movement Guide to Kinship with Ourselves and the Natural World

ELAINE COLANDREA

RORI SMITH

Epigraph Books
Rhinebeck, New York

ISBN 978-1-954744-74-5
Library of Congress control number: 2022908019
Cover Image: David Gilbert, *A Touch of Space*
Back Cover Image: David Gilbert, *Making Space*
Cover and Book Design by Colin Rolfe

Epigraph Books
22 East Market Street, Suite 304
Rhinebeck, NY 12572
EpigraphPS.com

The Elemental Body: A Movement Guide to Kinship with Ourselves and the Natural World is sponsored in part by Watermark Arts, an endeavor dedicated to art, education and community-building inspired and informed by somatic movement experience.

The images and poems in this book are protected under copyright of the individual artists. The authors are grateful for permission granted for use of the following:

Images:
A Touch of Space © David Gilbert
Merging © David Gilbert
Matrix © Prue Jeffries
Untitled 14 © Satya Kirsch
Untitled 17 © Satya Kirsch
Spilling Light 3 © Satya Kirsch
Spilling Light 1 © Satya Kirsch
Untitled © Satya Kirsch
Layered Light © Satya Kirsch
Untitled 11 © Satya Kirsch
Susan Harper & Emilie Conrad (1977) © Ron Peterson
Layered Light 2 © Satya Kirsch
Emergence © David Gilbert
Water & Light Milan © Prue Jeffries
Tree Wisdom (Rori Smith) © Brian Colleran
Potent Space © Prue Jeffries
Illuminato 7 © Barbara Schaefer
Seasonal Migration © Tuan Pham
Presence © David Gilbert
Clay II © Bethany Murray
Listening © David Gilbert
Clay III © Bethany Murray
San Jose, CA © Tuan Pham
Mycelium 1 © Binda Colebrook
Mycelium 3 © Binda Colebrook
Point Lobos, CA © Tuan Pham
Radiance © David Gilbert
Water & Light Comacchio 5 © Prue Jeffries
Fire 1 (Elaine Colandrea) © David Gilbert
Untitled 7 © Satya Kirsch
Fire 2 (Elaine Colandrea) © David Gilbert
Heart Passage © Gale Marsland
Earth Fever © Barbara Mindell
Flow 2 © David Gilbert
Water & Light Venice 1 © Prue Jeffries
Water & Light Porto Venere 2 © Prue Jeffries
Ocean Depths Fluidity © Barbara Mindell
Water & Light Venice 3 © Prue Jeffries
Tsunami © Tuan Pham
Moving Stillness © David Gilbert
Nerve © Barbara Mindell
Ground Found © David Gilbert
Intimacy with the Infinite © Shelley Ostroff
Spring © Shelley Ostroff

Sensuous 9 (Lumini Merced) © Carol Woolgar
Sensuous 3 (Lumini Merced) © Carol Woolgar
Sensuous 7 (Lumini Merced) © Carol Woolgar
Sensuous 10 (Lumini Merced) © Carol Woolgar
Dreamscape © Tuan Pham
Planet Play © David Gilbert
Making Space © David Gilbert

Poems:
Be The One © Raine Brown
Mystery of Being © Patricia Brown
The Unknown © Patricia Brown
Promise © Gisela Stromeyer
The Brooklyn Wind © Bobbie Ellis
Vying for Sunlight © Amber Elizabeth Gray
Breath of Air © Noelle Adamo
Every Dream Begins in Darkness © Amber Elizabeth Gray
Mother Earth © Noelle Adamo
Spring © Beth Pettengill Riley
The Soil of Myself © Raine Brown
Flying Fire © Gisela Stromeyer
Tongue of Fire © Noelle Adamo
Tenderness of Heart © Patricia Brown
Cosmic Blue © Noelle Adamo
Octaves © Noelle Adamo
Temper Me © Raine Brown
My Body of Water © Noelle Adamo
Like Water © Bobbie Ellis
Fluidity - Water Blessing for Our Time © Judi Bachrach
The Sea Walks © Judi Bachrach
The Five O'Clock Creek © Beth Pettengill Riley
Silent Night © Beth Pettengill Riley
Afternoon Emergence © Sandra Capellaro

Chapter opening quotations excerpted from:
Why Are You Here? © Penny Allport
Woman © Claudia Catani
Life on Land: The Story of Continuum © Emilie Conrad
Silver Lining - for COVID 19 © Amber Elizabeth Gray
Tongue of Fire © Noelle Adamo
The Well of the Lotus © Bobbie Ellis
The Breath of Winter © Beth Pettengill Riley

CONTENTS

Look for QR codes throughout *The Elemental Body*. Scan each individual code to access supplemental content that will enhance your reading experience. There are films to inspire your relationship with the elements and demonstration videos to accompany explorations, including a breath and sound demonstration for each chapter.

The QR code on this page will take you to the complete video library or you may visit www.watermarkarts.org/the-elemental-body-help-page.

ACKNOWLEDGEMENTS

What we share with you in *The Elemental Body* could not have come into its full being without the unfaltering support of the Watermark Arts creative team, our Continuum colleagues and the many contributions of Watermark Arts somatic artists.

Our visual senses adoringly regard the array of elemental expression in the works of art by Binda Colebrook, Brian Colleran, Prue Jeffries, Satya Kirsch, Gale Marsland, Lumini Merced, Barbara Mindell, Bethany Murray, Shelley Ostroff, Tuan Pham, Barbara Schaefer and Carol Woolgar, which provide points to pause and reflect as you traverse the landscape of creativity within and around you. We bow to David Gilbert for his exquisite collages, which, like the Muses, grace these pages to inspire your engagement with each elemental chapter.

We are grateful for the language of Watermark Arts writers Noelle Adamo, Penny Allport, Judi Bachrach, Patricia Brown, Raine Brown, Sandra Capellaro, Claudia Catani, Bobbie Ellis, Amber Elizabeth Gray, Beth Pettengill Riley and Gisela Stromeyer. Their poetry is imbued with palpable and sensate perceptions, providing another level of depth through which you may experience this book.

Our quandary about how to transmit a practice of embodiment without the presence of our living, breathing, moving bodies was resolved when colleague Beth Pettengill Riley, co-author of *A Moving Inquiry, The Art of Personal Practice*, suggested we augment our text with QR codes. Doing so has enabled us to incorporate digital resources and video demonstrations into the book, which dynamically enhance the transmission of the nuances embedded within the practice of Continuum.

The beautifully crafted films by Scott Furman, Prue Jeffries and Hannah Tobias feature Megan Bathory-Peeler, Claudia Catani, Mirco Dondi, Melanie Gambino, Prue Jeffries, Ed Rosenberg, Naomi Walker and members of Continuum Italia and Omega Institute workshops demonstrating and sharing their moving embodiments of Continuum. We thank Dario Dalboni, David Gilbert, Massimo Sacchi and Michael Schreiber, who served as videographers. We express our deep appreciation to composer Morena Boschetto for her original musical scores.

We owe the elegant form of the book to designer Colin Rolfe. We are encircled by the best of editors and readers Sandra Capellaro, Anne Deloria, Maryanne Gallagher, Bonnie Gintis and Beth Pettengill Riley, who have infused community on these pages.

Out of great passion to share Continuum with others and with enormous appreciation for our teachers and colleagues, we bring you a journey of discovery that has been expansive, enthralling and has taken us to new terrain, all of which we wish for you.

BE THE ONE

(EXCERPT)

Be the one with a brave heart
Be the one who opens wide your arms
Knows love to its fullest in your self
Lets it over flow all around you
Be the one who is free
Be the one who dances with delight
Lets radiance shine forth
Says this is who we are
This is our true nature

— RAINE BROWN

WELCOME

Now, it is time to embody nature.
— PENNY ALLPORT

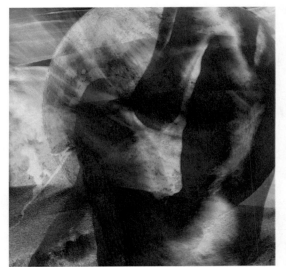

David Gilbert, *Merging*

The Elemental Body is an invitation to grow and tend a creative relationship with yourself and your environment. Each time you open these pages you drop a pebble of curiosity into the experiential pool of being and ride the gently expanding waves of discovery. With this book as your guide, you will craft a personal understanding of how the four elements essential to life: Air, Earth, Fire and Water, weave together within and around you. You will embody nature through movement, breath, sound and creativity. We hope this book will foster inquiry in all aspects of your being, awakening you to kinship with nature and the artistry in all life.

Why are the elements fertile ground for this adventure?

Air, Earth, Fire and Water are companions in our somatic inquiry, reflections of the material processes common to all living things.[1] Air is respiration, Earth is form and structure, digestion and decay, Fire is metabolism, Water is movement, evolution and the passage of time. These are only a few examples of how the world lives within the elements.

By invoking the elements, we lift the veil to a realm of exploratory play, to relationship with the hidden mysteries of the natural world. The elements are symbolic descriptions of the intricate connections that give rise to life on earth. Symbols act as portals to direct, holistic ways of perceiving, supporting our inquiry into making meaning out of complex systems.

As you explore your embodied self through the elements, trust your innate intelligence, deeply and wholly, as a source of understanding. Insight forms in the merging of your sensuous bodily experience with time for reflection and communication with yourself, peers and the world around you. Sourcing knowledge from sensory awareness informs all movement, from physical gestures, to the movement of thoughts and emotions. By slowing down to integrate this understanding within ourselves, we become freer to create, to collaborate and to better support others in these life-affirming acts.

[1] The term somatic refers to the experience of embodied sensation.

The Elemental Body is informed by Continuum, the movement inquiry process founded by visionary somatic pioneer and movement artist Emilie Conrad. Continuum is a quest to explore vastly, delve deeply and seek broadly.

What does it mean to be human? What is it to be fully alive? What are we here for?

Continuums helps us to recognize that we are not separate from the world around us. As biological beings, we are manifestations of nature. Nature is a varied and complex phenomenon. We choose the word "phenomenon" intentionally to evoke the marvelous and extraordinary character of direct sensory experience. The practice of Continuum is the experience of understanding yourself, through your own senses, as nature.

A distinct aspect of Continuum is that the practice is largely self-guided. Each sequence of movement inquiry is explored at one's own pace, in one's own way. *The Elemental Body* offers a movement map filled with landmarks to support your process of self-learning. This map is a flexible web that encourages discovering one's way into the unknown, where there is no one pathway, but instead a limitless terrain to be explored.

Awakening Your Elemental Self, video, 2 min.

Prue Jeffries, *Matrix*

MYSTERY OF BEING

Cultivate cellular listening
Be still and quiet in the beginning
sensing the breath
Allow space and time,
responding from the center.
Pause periodically.
Allow movement
to unfold naturally.
Take time.
Natural movement
arises from the
boundless
mystery of
Being…

— PATRICIA BROWN

Beauty, movement, nature and art are completely enmeshed in the journey you will take with this guidebook. The soul-stirring wonderment of life expressing itself - both intrinsic and extraordinary - is paramount in what we share with you.

The guided movement sequences in this book and the online demonstration videos, along with a lush collection of artwork and poetry, are designed for you to come alive to yourself as an indivisible expression of the elements. Absorb the colors, textures and tones of each work of art. Read the poems aloud and bathe in their vibrations.

Encountering the creative expression of others prepares you to appreciate yourself as living art. Art is a crystallization of the energy that animates life. Art allows us to communicate lived experience without diminishing or greatly altering its intuitive and sensory nature.

The Elemental Body supports the expression of life force, offering a place to land where your inherent creativity has the opportunity to blossom and move you. From whence you begin, may you be carried to the vast shores of yourself and beyond.

— ELAINE COLANDREA AND RORI SMITH

3

Unveiling Continuum, video, 3 min.

CONTINUUM

PRINCIPLES FOR SOMATIC PRACTICE

If I am water, I meet the thirst.
If I am fire, a dark night.
If I am wind, space.
If I am earth, I will meet the path.
— CLAUDIA CATANI

In Continuum we engage in sequences of breath, sound and fluid movement to slow perception, so that sensations from deep within may emerge. Direct sensory experience allows us to partner with the processes active within ourselves and intrinsic to all living systems.

Continuum, as a biological awareness practice, anchors human experience in an equitable relationship with all other life. With Continuum sound and movement explorations, we model, enact and re-enact biological systems from cellular physiology, embryology and evolution. To learn about growth and interdependence we become like the patterns common to these universal themes. We understand that our nature is a shared experience, integrated with the matter all around us. We recognize that our belonging to the world emanates from our innate living processes.

In her memoir, *Life on Land*, Emilie Conrad describes the felt experience of biological awareness:

> The concert of existence places me in resonance with our biosphere, meaning that at this moment there is no "body" no separation; I am part of the swirl of bio-morphic unfolding. I am not bound by culture or language. The deepening of sensation allows me to be without category. I transfer the moisture of my cells, join the wet of the grass, the pour of the ocean, the stars that watch over the night. The plants breathe, my skin is wet, we are here. This fundamental umbilical to life without category is for me the first stage of sanity (142-143).

Although Continuum is anchored in the tangible aspects of our being, it also encourages us to press against the boundaries of what cradles us to ask: *What do we not yet know about our own nature? What else exists to be discovered?*

Continuum allows us space to put our known selves aside and to take in just a little of the unknown at a time, by greeting the newness of each moment with wondrous observation. In this way, we avoid overloading our systems with too much new stimulus all at once. As Continuum teacher Priscilla Auchincloss says, "Overloaded systems lose their capacity for resilience."

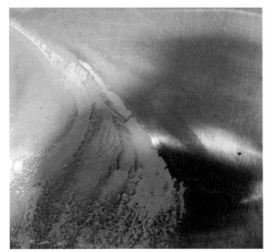

Satya Kirsch, *Untitled 14*

Satya Kirsch, *Untitled 17*

COMPONENTS OF CONTINUUM EXPLORATION

There are several components that shape a Continuum exploration. What follows is a brief description of each, accompanied by an opportunity for you to practice in order to enhance your understanding of the explanation.

BASELINE

A form of Open Attention, a period of noticing that precedes, pauses or follows a cycle of exploration. A baseline before beginning an exploration provides you with an initial point of reference. Later in the sequence, when you return to Baseline, you are more able to track changes in your experience. Noting what is new or different can expand your sensory vocabulary.

Take a moment, closing or lowering your eyes in order to bring your attention to your interior world - your breathing, your heartbeat, your contact with the surfaces around you. Notice movement in all its expressions - thoughts, feelings, sensations, impulses. Opening your attention inwardly cultivates presence - I am here; I am preparing for exploration.

BREATHING

Allow each inhalation and exhalation to come at its own pace. No two breaths need to be the same. It is beneficial to inhale through your nose, rather than your mouth. Your nasal passages are designed to filter air, preparing it for your lungs and signaling your nervous system to settle. The manner in which you shape your throat and mouth as you exhale will awaken different qualities in your being.

With your hands on your ribs, invite a dynamic relationship between the air in and around you. Notice the winds of exchange as you inhale and exhale.

SOUNDING[1]

Sound moves through space in waves. Each wave penetrates the varying densities of your body differently, creating a plethora of sensation. To experience sounding most potently, swallow your sound, directing the vibrations into yourself. Sound in your lowest natural register. Low frequency sounds have a regulating effect on the nervous system.

With eyes closed, exhale a low elongated hum and feel the vibrations in the substance of your body, your personal earthscape.

Satya Kirsch, *Spilling Light 3*

MOVING FLUIDLY

Fluid forms are present throughout every biological system within us; manifesting as blood, cerebrospinal fluid, cellular fluid, interstitial fluid, digestive fluid and lymphatic fluid. Intrinsic fluid movement is always occurring within your body in the form of arcs, curves, spirals and waves. Exploring the myriad expressions of our fluid anatomy is a primary component of Continuum. Moving slowly encourages every nuance of movement to be felt from within; every movement impulse is given time and space to reveal itself.

Blood spirals within the chambers of the heart and as it travels through arteries and veins. With your hands on your chest, feel the pulsation of your beating heart, your internal fire. Follow the pulsation rippling through you, carrying you into the watery realms of fluid movement.

Satya Kirsch, *Spilling Light 1*

OPEN MOVEMENT

By slowing down, resting and waiting, you clear the way for internal impulses to rise to the surface of your awareness. Letting go of deliberate task-based action, you may find yourself in a space of Open Movement, being moved in unpatterned response to your breathing and sounding. Like a leaf landing on a moving stream of water, your own fluid anatomy is carrying you into a state of creative flux, in which you are always changing.

Seated or standing with eyes closed, notice your position. Wait for the impulse to slowly shift into a new position. Pause and be present with yourself. Wait for a new impulse to change your position again. Pause again. Repeat, exploring yourself as a living sculpture continually forming and reforming, guided both by internal sensations and the space around you.

[1] Unless otherwise noted, all breaths and sounds in this guidebook were learned from Emilie Conrad.

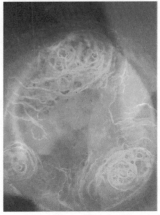

Satya Kirsch, *Untitled*

7

Satya Kirsch, *Layered Light*

Satya Kirsch, *Untitled 11*

RETURNING TO BASELINE

At the end of the sequence, pause. Notice your interior sense. Notice your sense of the world around you. Ask yourself, "What is moving in me now?" Many things may emerge for you in this space of Open Attention. Do not rush to make meaning. Instead, immerse yourself in the direct experience of what is unfolding for you.

LAYERING

After completing a Continuum sequence, you are encouraged to return to the beginning and repeat the breath, sound and movement series. Repeating the sequence deepens your sensory experience. With each layer, you create another opportunity for discovery and learning.

The components of Continuum exploration, as they combine within your practice, are prime expressions of communication.

To rest in the space of noticing is to say,
"I am open to dialogue."
To breathe is to converse with each cell in your being.
To sound is to hear yourself fully and
allow yourself to be heard.
To move fluidly, without expectation,
is to experience freedom and change.
To layer is to be receptive to all the places you have been,
all the places you may go and
the multiplicity of perspectives available to you as you continue.

Let these processes remind you of your unity with self, with others, with the earth and the cosmos. These skills engender an intimate relationship with all life and give meaning to your participation.

EXPANDING EMBODIED PRESENCE

Perceiving through our felt senses grounds us in the biological and physiological experience of being a *moving*, breathing human body. Universal growth motifs inherent to cellular, embryological and evolutionary processes become the pathways that widen our perception, bring new thoughts and ideas, resolve trauma, restore life force and broaden our definition of human potential.

At times in Continuum inexplicable experiences of enchantment occur. Exploration can take us into the imaginal realm of existence where visions, sounds, voices, feelings and memories emerge. Being present with your direct experience of the imaginal has the potential to be enlightening; unfolding your perception into creative discovery. In this place, you may come to understand yourself more wholly without attempting to make sense of or rationalize your experience.

Continuum explorations are vehicles of transformation to carry us into inquiry - moving inquiry. Like the fluid system on which Continuum is based, inquiries change over time in response to personal and societal needs. Evolution is beckoning. *How will you participate?*

Ron Peterson, *Susan Harper & Emilie Conrad (1977)*

Continuum has primarily existed as an oral tradition, passed from person to person, in a slowly widening circle. In the earliest years (1966-1974) Emilie Conrad was the sole conduit of Continuum. In 1975 she was joined by Susan Harper of Continuum Montage. Those of us who were their students received the guiding principles that form this unique movement inquiry process body-to-body, voice-to-voice and breath-by-breath in each moment of their transmission. Today, Continuum teachers around the world carry on this direct transmission and continue to evolve the practice.[2] Continuum itself is a living system.

[2] To locate a Continuum teacher near you visit: www.continuumteachers.com

THE UNKNOWN

How quickly the void
moves to be filled
with another's
ideas and ways to be.

How rare to surrender to
the void…
to a space and time
of no direction
no identity defining
the fabric of a life.

To simply stay in the Openness…

To be willing to watch
the tides of possibilities
roll in and out again.

To be willing to stay
in this uncomfortable
and unfamiliar ambiance

Until Openness, itself
is recognized as the only
true ground of Being.

— PATRICIA BROWN

YOUR JOURNEY

LIFTING THE VEIL ON EXPLORATORY PLAY

Breath, movement, sensation.
The song of the elements.
— EMILIE CONRAD

The Continuum explorations in *The Elemental Body* are organized into chapters: Air, Earth, Fire, Water and The Alchemy of the Elements, in which the four preceding chapters blend.

MOVEMENT INQUIRY

Each chapter begins with a short biological awareness exercise to enhance your perception of an element within yourself and your environment. These small morsels of direct experience transport you into the elemental fabric of your being. The chapter then expands upon this connection and further exploration sequences grow in complexity.

Longer explorations are presented in phases, which are designed to be practiced in layers. By repeating an exploratory sequence several times in a row, you drift away from habits and pre-planned action towards the unknown. When you layer a sequence, you cycle through form and formlessness. You enter a mutable state in which your fluid nature is revealed. The experience of mutability is one that helps us understand fluidity itself.

After layering a sequence and returning to baseline, take some time to digest the experience by asking yourself, "What did I find interesting?"

When we ask ourselves this question, we reflect upon our experience without assigning value of good or bad. Both positive and negative sensations can be interesting. What matters about your sensations is not whether they are positive, negative, comfortable, uncomfortable, familiar or new, but that there is the potential to learn from them.

Each time you return to an exploration, embrace your ability to have a completely fresh sensory experience. Direct sensory experience occurs only in the present.

Satya Kirsch, *Layered Light 2*

ARTFUL EMBODIMENT: CREATIVE RESPONSE

Immerse yourself in the variety of illustrative materials provided to prepare you for inquiry: the text, artwork and digital resources accessible through the QR codes in each chapter. A partnership of somatic exploration and creative engagement stimulates our curiosity. When curiosity is awakened, moving into the unknown is much more enticing.

Creating strengthens our ability to communicate and to share deep truths. Everyone benefits from creative acts. Along with increasing our self-knowledge, receiving the discoveries of others widens our understanding and broadens our capacity for compassion.

Within each chapter you will discover suggestions for processing your embodied observations and reflections through creative engagement such as collaging/collecting, drawing, gesturing, painting and writing. We invite you to frame this practice within the form of the mandala.

Mandalas are aesthetic tools on which to focus attention while contemplating the relationship to self, community and world. Traditionally, mandalas are circular forms containing geometric representations of a philosophical or spiritual space. The circular form of the mandala reflects a universal wholeness.

The mandala exercises suggested throughout the book are intended to embellish your creative play. The consistent circular form of each mandala maintains a continuity, a through-line, linking each of your experiences. All of your mandalas, together, form a collective, reflective body.

Before you begin an exploration, prepare a series of papers with one large circle drawn on each page. A large pot lid or plate can serve as a template for your mandala. Perhaps you will designate an Elemental Mandala Journal. We suggest a large spiral bound artist's pad containing quality paper that will accept multiple mediums: pencil, charcoal, pastel crayons and watercolor.

After completing an exploration, use the large circle on your paper as the space to create a mandala representing your experience. There is one set of mandala guidelines per chapter. Use those guidelines to create a mandala after any and all explorations within that chapter.

Using the symbolic language of art stimulates our awareness and curiosity in new ways. Your mandalas, archives of your sensory experience, will add layers of enrichment to your understanding.

MIRRORING NATURE
A Continuum Meditation in Movement

Mirroring Nature, video, 2 min.

WHAT WILL SUPPORT YOU AS YOU EXPLORE?

As an explorer on the move, it is useful to have portable tools that assist your inquiry and keep you comfortable.

INDOORS
- A quiet place free from distractions
- A thick mat, blanket or supportive surface to lie on
- Socks, layered clothing and extra blankets to ward off chill
- Additional pillows to support head and legs
- A stable chair without arms
- A notebook, sketch pad, writing/drawing implements or other artistic media you enjoy
- Water, to stay hydrated

OUTDOORS
- Attire to protect from seasonal elements (sun/heat, ticks/insects, cold, etc.)
- A blindfold (to protect the eyes on sunny days or to amplify senses other than sight)
- A thick mat or blanket (a sleeping pad is a lightweight choice) AND/OR
- A garden kneeling pad or two (to sit upon or place under hands/knees)
- A notebook, sketch pads, writing/drawing implements or other artistic media you enjoy
- A camera
- A receptacle for collecting natural materials
- Water, to stay hydrated

We encourage you to experience the explorations in a variety of locations in and around your home base. Engaging with Air, Earth, Fire and Water in an array of environments can shift your perspective, revealing pathways of connection and possibility.

Bon Voyage!

The biological processes always unfolding within you are inherently creative. A creative process is one in which something new is formed. In the body, these reformations happen as you breathe in oxygen and exhale carbon dioxide, as the food you consume is converted into nutrients and energy, as new cells grow and divide.

13

PROMISE

When you wake up in the morning
make a promise to yourself
that you will be a little
kinder today,
to yourself,
to others,
to the sky,
the air,
the water,
even the fire,
the animals and plants,
the life force in all things
and see
at the end of the day
what you have accomplished
and how you feel
about the day.

— GISELA STROMEYER

AIR

"The winds are the breath of the earth."
— ELAINE COLANDREA

*How do the movements of Air, within us
and around us, nourish our biology and our
imagination?*

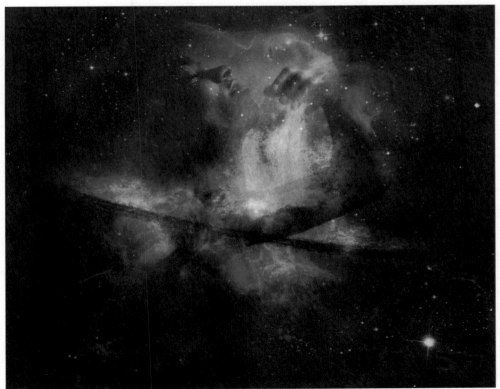

David Gilbert, *Emergence*

Breathing is the most primary and defining movement of human life. Drawing breath into our bodies, we notice our form and presence. With each inhalation, Air fills the vacuum of our lungs and diffuses through our bloodstream into each and every cell. As we exhale, our form momentarily dissolves. The fluid motion of inhaling and exhaling expresses the life cycle of the body in an ongoing dance between form and formlessness.

Breathing is an automatic process, but, as we experience in Continuum, it is possible to shape and tone the movements of breathing to enhance sensory feedback. For example, the relationship of inhalation to exhalation has a profound effect on the nervous system. While inhalations and exhalations of equal length cue the body for intense activity, an exhalation of slightly longer length than inhalation signals the body to deactivate its response to stress.

It is with breath that we recognize ourselves and regulate our being.

ATTUNING TO AIR IN THE OUTER LANDSCAPE

What is possible when we move with the flow of Air around us?

Observe the movements of Air above and around you.
Notice the contact of Air on your skin.
Listen to the wind song around you.
Enhance this exploration with the "Sh…" breath.
Inhale through your nose.
As you exhale, slowly and softly sound "Sh…"
Let the movement of Air move you. Dance with the wind.

REFLECTION
How has your outer awareness shifted after dancing with Air?
What do you notice internally?

ATTUNING TO AIR IN YOUR INNER LANDSCAPE

What is possible when we move with the internal expansiveness of breath?

With your hands on your ribs, notice the movement of your breathing.
Observe yourself for a few cycles of breath.
Inhale and as you breathe out, softly and slowly say "hah," elongating your exhalation.
Let the "hah" be a breath, rather than a voiced sound.
The "h" of the "hah" relaxes your tongue; the "ah" of the "hah" softens your jaw.
Repeat a few times at your own pace.
Then, bring your hands to your ribs and notice the movement of your breathing.
Let the movement of breath move you. Dance with your inner wind.

This exercise may help to reduce anxiety and bring you home to yourself.

REFLECTION
What do you notice about the spaces within yourself?
What do you notice about your relationship with the air and space around you?

THE BROOKLYN WIND

(EXCERPT)

The wind answers…Moving, changing…stop crying…Wipe your tears and remember
with reverence I know you and you know me and I know this and you know that
I look out my window and can no longer see the branches and the colors of the sky
Change, it is always happening around us, and yet?
I will go where I am called…intuitively called
Wind sweeps my consciousness…take me, please, I beg you

— BOBBIE ELLIS

Wind Dance III, video, 6 min.

AIR MANDALA

Language is a type of movement. It is one means by which
inner experience travels beyond the boundaries of what we call a
body. It is our breath that carries language outward into communication - with self and with others.

Starting with the words "I am," give voice to your felt experience. You may
begin this practice by naming sensations. Simile and metaphor can also help
you to describe your felt sense. Sometimes words will bubble forth freely,
other times it might be difficult to verbalize what you feel. Take your time.
Joining words with somatic experience is its own journey of discovery.

How does your verbal expression dialogue with your inner sense?
Fill the mandala circle with your "I am..." phrases. Create an "I am..."
mandala after each exploration as part of your Open Attention.
Explore how writing with different colors and mediums
relates to your embodied experience.

Tree Tryst, video, 7 min.

RECIPROCITY WITH OTHER LIVING SYSTEMS

Our breath is part of a symbiotic relationship with plants. Humans and plants are in mutual respiratory exchange at the cellular level. The oxygenated air we inhale is released from the cells of green plants. It is filtered and dispersed from our lungs, through our blood, to our tissues. The breath we release on exhalation contains carbon dioxide which in turn nourishes plant life.

Through sight or touch, connect with a green partner. Whether you are indoors or outdoors, a tree, shrub or houseplant may accompany you in this exploration. Rest comfortably noticing your state of being.

PHASE 1
- Inhale with the awareness that the plant is providing the oxygen that feeds your every cell. With each inhalation, sense your cells absorbing this essential nutrient for human life.
- Exhale with the awareness that your breath is giving the plant the carbon dioxide it needs to function.
- Continue this breathing exchange for a length of time that feels right to you.
- Return to noticing your state of being after this period of reciprocity.

REFLECTION
Has your breathing changed in any way?
What do you notice about your state of being?

Brian Colleran, *Tree Wisdom (Rori Smith)*

PHASE 2

Continuum breaths deepen and refine your experience. Repeat the Phase 1 practice, adding the specific inhalations and exhalations below.

- Purification Inhalation: Gently draw the sides of your nose slightly downward to narrow the flow of air into your nasal passages. This slowing down of the movement of air into your body will allow you more time to notice what occurs with every inhalation: the multitude of movements, shifts and changes.
- Stream Exhalation: Release the sides of your nose. Exhale lightly shaping "F…" with your lips. This shape creates a narrow stream of breath, which slows down your exhalation and encourages you to complete each outbreath, allowing your breath to fully exchange with the environment.
- You may wish to repeat this cycle of breath three or more times and notice any changes in yourself.

PHASE 3

- Follow the movement of your breathing into open exploration with your green partner.
- Allow the Purification Inhalation and Stream Exhalation to come and go as you move your body, intuitively layering these breaths as needed to support and inspire you.

PHASE 4

- At the end of your movement practice, settle into stillness to notice what is nurtured in you.

REFLECTION

Take time to offer your appreciation to your green partner.

BRANCHING: NOURISHMENT AND COMMUNICATION

Branching is a pattern of communication, of informational exchange. It is a way for any system to avail itself of increasing amounts of nourishment and to disperse nutrients across a broader area. The pattern of dividing or splitting to both reach and receive is visible in our overall skeletal structure and hidden deep within our bodies. Branching patterns make up the structure of our circulatory, nervous and respiratory systems.

Branching is not only an effective source of receiving and distributing nourishment, it is a means of decentralizing power and energy throughout a system.

Brian Colleran, *Tree Wisdom (Rori Smith)*

PHASE 1: OUTER NATURE OBSERVATION

- Spend some time observing the central axis of a tree or plant.
- Observe the spreading patterns that grow from the central axis through the plant's branches, stems and leaves.
- You may want to make a sketch, take photographs or trace the branching patterns with gesture.

PHASE 2: INNER NATURE OBSERVATION

- Bring your attention to your torso. Notice your limbs emerging from your central body.
- While sounding a low "hum," let movement arise in your torso. Ride the "hum" vibration into movement that branches from your torso, to your limbs, out into your fingers and toes.
- Let the movement from your extremities return back into your central body.
- Explore the reciprocal exchange between your torso and limbs.

REFLECTION

As you settle into stillness, what do you notice about yourself?
What do you notice about your attention to the flow of information within and around you?

VYING FOR SUNLIGHT

Branches long upward
Mist. Beam. Air. Rooting to sky.
Life rewards the reach

— AMBER ELIZABETH GRAY

Prue Jeffries, *Potent Space*

SPACE: THE EXISTENTIAL MOTHER

We owe the description of space as our existential mother to Emilie Conrad. Her words invite us to recognize support in the unseen: the atomic and cosmic realms that suspend our terrestrial bodies within the spectrum of the infinitesimal to the infinite. The element of Air awakens us to the sensible qualities of the atmosphere we inhabit. Air draws our attention to the potency of space, around and within our bodies.

How can partnering with space support us in movement?

Brian Colleran, *Tree Wisdom (Rori Smith)*

Air Breath & Sounds,
demonstration video,
7 min.

CAVE WIND BREATH

The Cave Wind Breath[1] offers an entryway into our internal spaciousness. This breath evokes the wind traveling through natural caves, which contain a variety of spaces - some narrow, some deep, some wide. Let this breath travel internally, through the caves of your mouth, skull, throat, rib cage, pelvis, even the channels within your bones. The ever-changing shaping of this breath shifts your being in innumerable ways.

- Inhale through your nose.
- In one stream of exhaled breath, form your mouth, tongue and lips to create many different vowel shapes.
- Allow the shaping of your breath to become more varied with each exhalation.
- Notice how the inner spaces of your body respond to your breath.

Prue Jeffries, *Water & Light Milan*

[1] This breath was learned from Susan Harper of Continuum Montage.

CLOUD WALKING – CREATING INTERNAL BUOYANCY

Spend some time observing clouds. Clouds are collections of water molecules in the atmosphere. Notice how Air shapes and moves the clouds. Notice the variations in the density of clouds, throughout the sky and on different days, as the water molecules that form them collect and disperse through Air.

In clouds we observe Air as a fluid field. Fluids are any substances that change shape according to the boundaries of what contains them. Just as your body may float when in water, cloud bodies float in the fluidity of Air. In this exploration, draw your attention to Air as a buoyant fluid. Noticing this quality in the space around you will shift your perception of your own weight and allow your body to be held in effortless movement by Air.

For this exploration, having your seat lifted off the ground will be of value. If you are indoors, explore while seated on a chair. If you are outside, explore from a natural perch, like a boulder or fallen log.

-   Anchor your hands and feet on the ground, on your chair or somewhere on your body. They may even support one another, your palms or the soles of your feet touching.
-   Let the Cave Wind Breath penetrate your core body - your head, chest and belly. Allow time for your core body to ceaselessly flow, the way clouds alter form and are moved by Air. Allow time to sense your body buoyant with breath-filled shape shifting.
-   Next, channel the spacious quality of the Cave Wind Breath from your core body into your limbs.
-   Your limbs will begin drifting into space, away from contact with your body. Take time to let each limb, alone or in combination with other limbs, emerge within the balance of internal weight and external support. At this stage, you may feel that your head and tail express themselves as limbs. Once all of your limbs are in active play, bring your attention to the air around you.

CLOUD WALKING – EXPLORING THE POTENCY OF SPACE AROUND US

Cloud Walking,
demonstration video,
5 min.

- Begin by tuning into the space between your fingers.
- With a closed mouth, shape your throat as if you were going to "hum" and slowly exhale breath up the back of your throat, to your soft palate. This is the Lunar Breath.
- Let the space between your fingers, the Air itself, expand or shrink with this silent sound. Evoke the sense of being moved, the way clouds are moved by the wind.
- Next, bring your attention to the space between your arms and your core body. Continuing the Lunar Breath, activate the space between your body and your arms. Similar to the way a breeze lifts leaves on a tree, let your limbs be lifted by the Air encircling you. Sense yourself becoming lighter.

Continue this exploration with the Lunar Breath and other spaces around you:

- between your other limbs and core body
- between one limb and another
- between your body and your seat
- between your body and the ground

Let the space around you, the Air around you, support your limbs. The Lunar Breath will help you slow down and attune to space supporting you in suspension, space moving you. Imagine yourself as a cloud "walking" - limbs being moved by the changing air-filled space.

You may wish to turn your torso horizontally to gravity, coming sideways on the seat of your chair or boulder, with one hand/arm in contact with the ground. This supported side-lying position will let your legs "walk" in the clouds, exploring slow, fluid motion. Spend some time on one side and then on the other.

We don't normally walk from a side-lying position. This new relationship to gravity allows novel ways of sensing and moving.

At the end of your exploration, settle in a resting position.

REFLECTION

What do you notice about your sense of weight and your sense of space?
Name qualities that describe the space inside of you.
Name qualities that describe your relationship to the space around you.

Barbara Schaefer, *Illuminato 7*

BREATH OF AIR

My breath travels the edges of everything.
It knows the shapes of diffusion and density, agony and ecstasy.
The spaces within me contain it the way a hummingbird contains the moment,
while the lungs and bones tone together then blossom
while the heart unfurls within its nest
while the skin discovers sight and mobility
while the mind tingles with dissolve
while the eyes fertilize the world with tears.
Even without a sound my breath of air makes music.
With it I am Krishna's flute, song of my father.
I carry the seeds of my father and grandfathers further than myself
before returning to the inhale, then the exhale.
I exist in the center of its comings and goings even when the center is off
and still it cradles me just as when I first was born.
Even with no tools my breath of air creates.
With it I am Earth's mandala, a shifting kaleidoscope,
a puzzle with no pieces, allowing the unknown to exist.
My mother's mother's diaphragm did the same thing,
and mine now still finds new ways to model the world.

I sense the pulse of a sun-warmed stone,
the release of a tree trunk against my back.
There's only so much of this life I can take in
before I must let it go, but my breath does not let me cling.
The wind gathers strength in branches bare to its power.
My breath gets tossed and alerts me
to the multiplicity of shadows. I can stay or go.
My breath is a nomad on an ever-changing landscape.
It lifts me, places me, locates me here, then over there.
It compasses a way through September's tall grasses.
It is the wave that finds all water.
Where it goes I follow, where I am it returns.
When I'm not paying attention, I sink, I rise,
while my breath meanders, replies to lovers, unmasks the wanting,
then curls back and embraces me again.
Together, we are wave and body and boat.
There is no alone. I see you night-sailing
in the meadow too.

— NOELLE ADAMO

Tuan Pham, *Seasonal Migration*

EARTH

Earth breathes: Sigh. Relief.
Humans, be still. Listen. Your
heart beats strong in mine.
— AMBER ELIZABETH GRAY

David Gilbert, *Presence*

How do we deepen our connection to Earth, our primal home?

Air assists us in discovering the upper and outer realms of nature to feel the uninterrupted exchange of breath with all life around us. Earth stewards us beneath the surface, to a realm of rooting and supporting. Earth supports structures - landforms, built environments, bodies - and it supports generative processes. Earth is the site of creative fertile ground and of the dormancy and decay necessary for new growth to emerge.

Your body is a landscape and a microcosm of its own. The forms and features of your external body shape a visual representation of you, which changes with the seasons and with the passage of time, just as the terrain around you cycles through growth, hibernation and rebirth. Your body is layered with skin, fat, fascia, muscle, bone and connective tissue that swaddles and supports your organs, your centers of heat and energy, just as the earth's layers of crust and mantle surround a fiery core.

In the Heart of the Cave, video, 3 min.

EARTH DUET

Let yourself be drawn to the earth, even a small section of soil will do.
Stand quietly and send your energy through the soles of your feet into the earth.
Sense the currents of Earth energy rising,
through your feet, legs, core body, arms and head.
Let your arms fill and branch out.
Move from the Earth energy within you.
When you are ready, stand quietly again, notice the Earth dance living in you.

EARTH MANDALA

To prepare yourself to craft your Earth mandalas, gather a collection of natural materials. Nature's bounty abounds in leaves, petals, stems and roots, shells, soil, sticks and stones. After each exploration in the Earth chapter, allow yourself to spontaneously assemble a mandala from your collection of natural treasures. You may wish to record your assemblages in photographs, drawings or paintings.

David Gilbert, *Listening*

EVERY DREAM BEGINS
IN DARKNESS

Feet kneading dark loam
Sifting debris stirs new blooms.
These seeds harbor hope.

— AMBER ELIZABETH GRAY

FINDING GROUND, BEING FOUND

PHASE 1
- Standing quietly, bring your hands to rest on your belly, the center of your own bodily landscape.
- As you inhale, feel your belly shifting form, expanding outward.
- As you exhale, notice your belly softening inward, emptying.
- Continue this for several breaths.

PHASE 2
- Add the sound of "O." Inhale through your nose, then exhale a low continuous "O" sound. Attend to the full shape of the "O" in your throat, the fullness of your belly and the fullness of Earth's body.
- Direct the "O" - a continuous tube of vibratory sound - down one leg, through your foot and into the ground. Envision the vibration of the sound as a manifestation of gravity passing through you.
- Repeat a number of times with that leg, followed by time in quiet presence.
- Direct the "O" sound down your other leg, through your foot and into the ground.
- Repeat as many times as feels right.

PHASE 3
- In this phase, reverse the direction of your "O" sounds.
- Taking your time, draw the "O" up from the earth through each foot and leg into the pool of your belly.
- When you feel full of Earth energy, begin to move slowly, letting the sensation spread upwards in your torso, arms and head. Become Earth dancing.

PHASE 4
- After your dance, take time in quiet presence with yourself and the ground below you.
- Make an offering of gratitude to acknowledge your relationship with Earth.

Bethany Murray, *Clay II*

REFLECTION
What do you notice about your legs and feet?
What do you notice about your relationship with the ground?

REFLECTION
What do you notice in your relationship with your core body?
What do you notice in your relationship with Earth's body?

INNER CANYONLANDS

Bethany Murray, *Clay III*

Your core body, from head to tail, comprises three semi-spherical territories: the pelvic bowl, the rib cage and the skull. Dark, deep and voluminous are the complex internal landscapes of these personal canyonlands. Tissues folding, sloping, winding and coiling into the ecosystems that support your wellbeing.

Waterways can often be found at the base of canyons. It is the movement of water that carves many canyons into existence. As long as water is present in a landscape, it will continue to meld with and shape the porous earth, providing respite and sustenance to animals and plants. Even deep in the ocean floor, underwater canyons are protective spaces that cradle exceptional biodiversity.

PHASE 1

- Lying or seated in a restful position, begin with breath. Gently inhale and exhale through your nose. Feel the inner surface of your body as your internal volume adjusts with each breath.
- Allow yourself to be drawn to an inner canyon: the pelvis, rib cage or skull. As breath moves into and through you, notice the inner terrain of this cavity.
- Fill the chosen cavity with 3-6 low Puffed "O" sounds. To shape the Puffed "O," softly draw your lips together to allow only a small aperture for breath to escape. Allow your exhalation to puff your cheeks full, to move the tissues of your mouth in a voluminous manner. Explore the rebounding of your sound within, as your voice would echo against the walls of a deep crevasse.
- Notice the vibration throughout the chosen cavity and the tissues that comprise its boundaries.

Notice what emerges from the meeting of sound and body. You may wish to rest or to follow movement impulses to explore the nooks and crannies of the space within you.

Repeat Phase 1 in all three territories - pelvis, rib cage and skull - in a sequence that feels right to you.

OPTIONAL PRACTICE CONTEXTS

- Explore blindfolded, noticing the influence of darkness on your bodily experience.
- Alternatively, situate yourself in a sunny indoor spot or outdoors on the warmth of the earth or a large stone. Notice the influence of light.

PHASE 2

- Begin a Puffed "O" sound in your pelvis.
- Travel with the Puffed "O" through your body until you reach your skull. The journey may happen in the course of one exhalation or it may take several exhalations.
- The journey may inspire movement; ride the movement until you come again to still-ness.
- Repeat as many times as feels right to you. You may feel satisfied or you may wish to reverse the cycle, traveling from skull to pelvis.

REFLECTION

What do you notice about your relationship to the inner landscape of your body?
What do you notice about the borderlands of your body?

PHASE 3

- Allow yourself to be drawn again to one of the three cavities for exploration.
- Place your hands lightly on the midline of the chosen cavity. Rest, attuning to the fluids within that part of your body. You may connect to a felt sense of fluidity or you may be assisted by your imagination.
- When you are ready, begin a slow hissing "S" breath. Sustaining the "S," bring your tongue to lightly rest between your upper and lower teeth, like you are shaping a "Th" sound.
- You may also find your way into this breath by reversing the component parts, begin-ning a "Th" exhalation and layering on the shape of "S."
- As you sound, glide your touch from your midline outward.
- Repeat 3-6 times in each of the three core body cavities.
- Explore the porosity of your own boundaries.

PHASE 4

- Rest in open attentive awareness.

As your breath slips out, it spreads and dissolves over both your inner and outer landscape. The river of your exploration meets the banks of you and is absorbed beyond the container of your body and into the whole of the earth.

REFLECTION

What qualities do you notice in the canyons of your body?
What do you notice in the meeting of touch and body?

MOTHER EARTH
(EXCERPT)

*…because my body is of earth
and knows things I don't dare deny –
the intelligence of the senses
and the catalogue of evolution,
fragile as a teardrop.*

— NOELLE ADAMO

Tuan Pham, *San Jose, CA*

Stone Teachings,
demonstration video,
6 min.

STONE TEACHINGS

Gather stones of different sizes. Your body will be in contact with these stones through-out this exploration. For comfort, warm the stones so that they are a pleasant tempera-ture. Outdoors, the stones may be heated by the sun. Indoors, you may heat the stones in warm water or by wrapping them in a heating pad. Test the temperature of the stones before placing them on your body.

PHASE 1

- Lie down in a comfortable position with your stones nearby.
- Take a few moments to settle. No-tice which parts of you are in contact with the surfaces below you. Notice the flow of your breath and attention through various parts of your body. Notice places where you feel con-stricted, places where you feel softly released.

You are collecting information about your bodily landscape, like an explorer in a new territory.

Tuan Pham, *Point Lobos, CA*

PHASE 2

- Place stones on your body: at your belly, at your breast bone, at your forehead. You may even want to slip the stones between your skin and clothing. Hold a stone in the palm of each hand.
- Be present with the weight of each stone.
- Bring attention to your bones, the most mineralized part of your connective tissue.
- Take time in quiet presence with yourself.

Earth Breath & Sounds, demonstration video, 5 min.

Bones are the part of your body most similar to stones, where gravity can be most readily felt.

PHASE 3: ADDING VIBRATORY SOUND

- Sound "Z" for the length of an exhalation.
- Sound "J," as in the name "Jacques," for the length of an exhalation.
- Alternate between "J" and "Z" in one exhalation.
- Let your sounding be directed internally.
- After a period of sounding, return to observing your felt sense.

REFLECTION
What do you notice about your bones?
What do you notice about your relationship to the surfaces beneath you?

PHASE 4: MOVING WITH STONES AND GRAVITY

The invisible force of gravity unites your body in partnership with the weight of the stones above you and the contact of the ground below you.

- Press downward through the places in you that are touching the ground.
- As you press into the places of contact, notice the response in other parts of your body. Pressing in one part of the body may create a spreading lift in other parts of you.
- Let the pressing flow through you, taking you into movement discovery.
- The stones in your hands and on your body will also influence your movement, allowing you to press upward into their weight and to feel their weight press upon you in return.
- Reintroduce the "J-Z" sound as you continue to explore pressing.

REFLECTION
What arose in you that you found supportive?
Are you aware of the support from the ground, from the air and space around you?
Can you sense your sound and breath as a form of support?

PHASE 5

- When you are done, notice your bones, all the rest of you and your sense of the ground.

SPRING
(EXCERPT)

Uprising out of dense Earth
thick with dark, wet mud –
a pulse, a gurgling –
the origin of life, begins again
to unfold, unfurl
the momentous occasion of a flower –
not to be seen as a flower at first –
just a ripple in the mud.

— BETH PETTENGILL RILEY

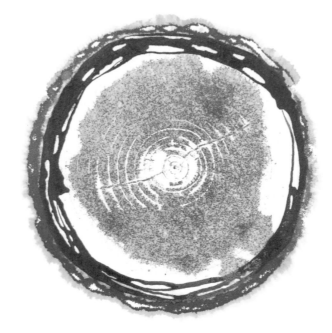

Binda Colebrook, *Mycelium 1*

Piezoelectric Energy Exploration, video, 3 min.

PIEZOELECTRIC ENERGY EXPLORATION

The movement of molten fluids within the earth's core transfers energy through its layers. This fluid movement is one possible way in which the surface of the earth changes form over time. As large plates of land are carried into contact with one another, patterns of folding and compression are created.

You can see the effects of this resistance and pressure in both the topography and the stratification of the land around you. Rolling hills, deep valleys and high, craggy mountains are all visible examples of the earth's crust folding and unfolding onto itself. In the layers of soil that build up with time, you can see the history of this earthen dance.

When pressure is applied and our bodies move against resistance, there is an increase in a specific energy known as piezoelectricity. Moving against resistance is a primary way our bones, fascia, muscles, tendons and ligaments are strengthened. Piezoelectric energy provides the body with feedback that stimulates the generation of new, healthy tissue.

Binda Colebrook, *Mycelium 3*

In Phase 4 of Stone Teachings, you began to explore full contact with the ground. You merged with the properties of the soil or stone landscape and were invited to feel the substance of your own being in contact with that of another. This practice cultivates a sense of belonging, fulfilling a primary need to locate yourself, to know where you are, that you exist with full sensory presence.

This enhanced kinesthetic awareness is useful in practical situations, like avoiding accidental hazards in your path or safely recovering your own weight during a fall. It can also have beneficial psychological effects, encouraging you to relate to your own identity in the present moment, rather than past experiences. It may lead you to regard the natural world as more animate, like you, than ever before.

Develop your sensory presence further by attuning yourself to the transformational potential you receive from Earth through the energy of pressing. The "J-Z" sound can help you to channel a vibratory connection between your body and the ground.

This exploration can be done in many different positions. Each one will offer a novel relationship to gravity, which will engage you in different ways, offering many opportunities for whole body strengthening and deepening your sense of sharing energy with the earth. Indoors, the floor, a sturdy chair and a wall will be helpful to you. Outdoors, the ground, trees and boulders can all provide surfaces to press upon.

PHASE 1

- Lie on your back with your knees bent and your feet grounded firmly on the floor.
- Sound "J-Z," exploring varying degrees of pressure from the soles of your feet into the surface below you. Take time to journey around the complete landscape of the sole of your foot, with all its hills and valleys.
- Observe the effects of pressing your feet into the ground throughout your body. You may notice the coursing of energy up your legs. You may find your pelvis moving in response.

PHASE 2

- As the exploration from your feet settles, sound "J-Z" as you press your pelvis into the ground.
- Take time to journey around the complete landscape of your pelvis.
- Observe the effects of pressing your pelvis into the ground throughout your body. You may notice the coursing of energy down your legs and/or up your spine. You may find your limbs and spine rippling away from the pressure of your pelvis, as the waves of piezoelectric energy dissipate through you.
- Use only the degree of pressure that feels right to you, which may change from moment to moment. *How does the rest of your body respond?*

PHASE 3

- Continue this process with the other parts of your body that are in contact with the surfaces below you. Roll the pressure from location to location, following your own impulses.
- Move slowly, finding trails and creating new ones where they did not exist before.

Roll/press your way to your side, your belly and into other positions:

- Seated or standing with your torso against a wall.
- On hands and knees, which may grow up to hands and feet and, eventually, to standing.
- You might use a wall, chair or other stable surface to "walk press" up to standing, pressing your hands into the wall and pressing your feet into the ground.
- Feel free to explore in unusual ways, like pressing your hands into the ground and your feet against a wall or other stable surface.

As often as you are called to, pause in silent, still presence to absorb your tissues' responses to pressure. These moments of rest will allow the fluids within you that have been invigorated by pressing to penetrate more deeply into your cells, amplifying your body's natural rhythms of absorption and release.

REFLECTION

What have you discovered by merging your bodily landscape with the landscape around you?

THE SOIL OF MYSELF

I stand

I weep

I cry

Tears, which for months have contained, pain, despair, confusion, doubt

now express relief, release from an ordeal, a journey of burrowing deep

into ground packed hard by a lifetime of beliefs and patterns

Now the soil of myself has been harrowed, ploughed, turned over,

revealed, fresh, moist, broken open and apart

I smell the earthiness

I smell the darkness exposed towards light

I touch the dirt. Pick it up in my hand, earth, soil, ground.

What is this really? What is this matter from which life can emerge?

Place a seed within its mystery and that which has been silent, dormant

gracefully emerges like some sort of magic

Roots pushing down, deep and deeper

A stem, fine and delicate, reaches up through the dark folds

feels the sun, feels the rain, feels the wind

What a wonder it must be to move from tight encasement of seed

to a form pushing down, reaching up,

taking into the senses the feel and support of the darkness below

the pull of the light and rain above

the calling up, the invitation down and deep

What is the consciousness of this experience?

What is the feeling of this awakening?

I allow my senses to embody the vision, delve into the question.

I feel a smile spread across my face as my being reaches towards the light

awakens to new and wondrous sensations.

I feel my feet and toes send tendrils down into the ground

I feel nourishment flow up from the mysterious dark matter

Mother Earth feeding me life.

I feel my spine, twist, turn, roll, reach, as I grow towards the sun.

I feel limbs and leaves reach out from my sides. I feel them strengthen

as the breeze and winds swirl around me, playing, inviting me to dance, to sway

to hear the song of my own self as the wind plays and whistles through my limbs.

The rain falls and gathers on my leaves. I feel them grow heavy, bow and bend

as the water channels on their center veins, drops to the ground around my base

seeps into the porous earth, is drunk up by my roots, pulled up through my deep channels.

I am nourished by that which traced and journeyed across my own body.

I am awed by the cycle of support. Its simple beauty.

My trunk grows strong, tall. My roots go deep and deeper, connecting with more

and more earth, reaching out for more and more support as I grow. I am connected

to all around me. Soil, earth, water, wind, sun, all growing and living things.

Amazed each moment by the wonder of it all.

— RAINE BROWN

FIRE

In each and every utterance
unleashed
my voice sounds out
I am here,
for however long it takes
to burn
— NOELLE ADAMO

What sparks your curiosity; what ignites you?
Is Fire at the heart of the creative spirit?

Fire is the great transformer. Whatever Fire touches is altered forever by the intensity of its blaze. Yet, Fire is a vital part of life's rhythm. Fire can be beneficial to renewal, clearing from an environment what is no longer needed, so that new growth has light, air and nutrients to thrive. By tending your internal fire, you reveal the terrain from which your most essential self can move.

Light is a manifestation of Fire that instigates physiological processes in our bodies. Sunlight warms us up on cold days, stimulates the production of vitamin D and helps us to absorb other vital nutrients. Lack of sunlight can negatively affect our mood, cognition and energy levels. Exposure to the changing moonlight throughout the lunar cycle also influences our energy and mood. During full moons, the excess of moonlight may cause us to sleep less deeply, but this light also beckons us to view our world from a different perspective. Tracking the movements of the moon is one way we mark the passage of time.

In this next exploration, in the course of one day, nurture your relationship with the sun and the moon.

David Gilbert, *Presence*

RECEIVING THE LIGHT OF THE SUN, RECEIVING THE LIGHT OF THE MOON

Indoors by a window or outdoors in nature,
settle into a restful position and invite light into your cells.
Allow yourself time simply for receiving.
Receiving is an act in itself.
To receive light, allow your body to soften.
Layer by layer,
through skin and muscle,
and all the membranes swaddling your skeleton,
invite light to melt deeply into you.

REFLECTION
*As you emerge from the process of receiving, do
you notice changes in yourself?
Name the qualities of your sun-warmed being.
Name the qualities of your moonlit being.*

Chiaroscuro, video, 6 min.

FIRE MANDALA

Use charcoal – purchased from an art supply store or gleaned from the cooled embers of a fire – to create a mandala after each exploration in this chapter.

As you emerge from exploration, draw a single, continuous and spontaneous gesture within the mandala circle. Let the impulse from within guide your movement.

FLYING FIRE

Tonight I stepped into the dark night,
naked
I left the day behind and moved
without fabric skin
into the dark presence
as is.
I am here! I have come! I shout
Where are you,
all you magical creatures…?
Where are you, wind of spirit and
waving trees…?
I am here
Naked with my heart of pure love!
And slowly they show up all
around me,
they have been dancing all
night long
with their shining light.
Flying with fire.

— GISELA STROMEYER

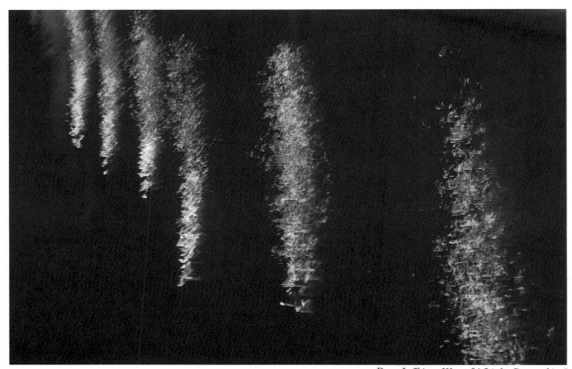

Prue Jeffries, *Water & Light Comacchio 5*

MIRRORING THE MOVEMENT OF FLAMES

Sit with a fire or a burning candle. Notice the myriad stages of the flame's shape and substance. Sense each change within you.

The flame moves in relation to its environment. As the density of the surrounding air decreases in response to the heat, bursts of energy are released, visible in the fire's shimmering dance as it is fueled, made more vital, by the air. You are witnessing the flame during its own processes akin to respiration and sensory exploration. Notice the inextricable partnership of elements as Fire cannot exist without Air.

David Gilbert, *Fire 1 (Elaine Colandrea)*

THE "LA"

Breathe in through your nose. As you exhale through your mouth, allow the tip of your tongue to strike and release from the roof of your mouth while repeatedly sounding "LA." Like the spontaneous patterns of a dancing flame, sound "LA" with unplanned variations in speed and rhythm as you exhale. Continue to observe the burning wood or candle, focusing your attention on the flickering tips of the flames.

- "LA" activates the tongue as a gateway to the core body. Allow the "LA" sound to resonate from your tongue's tip to its root in the mid-throat, then swallow the sound into your gut body. The engagement of your abdominal muscles and diaphragm while sounding "LA" creates intensity and builds up internal heat.
- After a period of sounding, encourage your core body to respond in open movement.
- As you move freely, notice your breath and its relationship to your inner fire until you feel called to rest.

Would you recognize a log and the burnt ashes from that log as the same substance?

REFLECTION
What sensations arose in you during the exploration? And afterward?
Make an offering to the flame - Fire's dancing spirit.

TONGUE OF FIRE
(EXCERPT)

Tongue of fire kissed by the breath,
alive in this body
every shape a neural message
bowed to its versatile theater.

— NOELLE ADAMO

David Gilbert, *Fire 2 (Elaine Colandrea)*

THE HEART, YOUR INNER FIRE

Blood circulates through our hearts in a continual spiral. The pulsing of cardiac muscle and the heart's outward flowing vessels spread warm, oxygenated blood throughout our bodies, making the heart our personal fire center. Our circulatory system then returns blood in need of oxygen to our lungs and heart. The heart is the keystone in this bodywide system of fluid exchange.

SOUNDS FOR THE NEXT EXPLORATIONS:

"VUH"[1] – As you exhale, rest your upper teeth lightly on your lower lip while sounding an extended "V" vibration. Simultaneously shape your jaw and throat in a continuous "UH" breath. Together the low, idling, vibratory sound of "VUH" is created.

The combined sounds in "VUH" bathe the heart, transmitting vibrations down your lower lip, jaw and throat in the direction of your chest cavity, where your heart and lungs are nestled.

"O" – At the back of your mouth, shape your throat into the open form of an "O." Extend the "O" sound, in a middle to low tone for the length of your exhalation.

If you could see the shape of your sound, you would see a tubular form. Throughout nature tubular forms are effective means of fluid transportation. In your body, fluids wash through the tubular forms of your intestines, blood vessels and central nervous system.

"E" – Form your mouth and lips to say "E." Exaggerate the widening of the corners of your mouth to emphasize the lateral quality of the "E" sound. Using a low tone, extend the "E" sound as you exhale.

The shape of "E" has a sheath-like, spreading quality, much like your skin stretching across the surface of your body. Sheaths serve as cases for collections of related biological material. Fascia, the network of sensory tissue that surrounds every muscle, bone, organ and nerve in the body, shares this form and is integral to feeling our own movement.

In sounding "O" and "E," we sing a biological lullaby to the relatedness of natural forms within us and around us.

[1] This version of the "VUH" sound is as taught by Elaine Colandrea. Other variations exist.

CIRCULATING FROM THE HEART EXPLORATION

Settle onto your back with your hands resting on the region of your heart. Take time to become aware of your heart's movement pulsing from within.

Circulating from
the Heart,
video, 5 min.

PHASE 1

- Bathe your heart in "VUH" vibrations.
- Pause as needed to be present with yourself and your response.

PHASE 2

- Extend your arms and legs into a starfish position.
- From your heart, sound "O." Direct the resonant "O" through your torso to the end of one of your limbs. You may take more than one "O" to cover the distance.
- When you have completed one limb, return to your heart to spread "O" down the next limb. Continue until all your limbs have been explored to your satisfaction.
- You may want to repeat each limb more than once. You may notice a sensation of length or extension as you sound into each limb.

PHASE 3

- Come to a position in which all your limbs are curled inward towards your heart.
- While sounding "E," allow your limbs, individually or simultaneously, to radiate outward from your heart and then return inward. Some of your limbs may be radiating out while others are returning in, allowing your movements to layer atop themselves.
- As you fall deeper into the rhythms of circulatory exchange, explore initiating whole body radial movement from your heart with the expansive quality of the "E" sound.

PHASE 4

- Allow yourself to settle back into your baseline. Rest in open attentive awareness.

REFLECTION

What are you noticing about your innermost being?
What are you noticing about your periphery?
Your peripheral body? Your peripheral attention?
What are you noticing about the whole of you?

THE ELECTROMAGNETIC FIELD OF THE HEART

The pulsating movement of the heart creates a powerful electromagnetic field. This field extends in a radius beyond our bodies, emanating outward in ever-changing, arcing waves of energy. The heart's capacity for communication is embedded in this fluctuating wave motion, which weaves through the very fabric of our physical world.

Engaging as embodied researchers of the heart, we ask questions that are central to wellbeing and to the intimate bonds we form with one another. *Does the heart's field reflect the qualities of the person from whom it originates? Does it interact with the heart fields of other beings?*

Satya Kirsch, *Untitled 7*

RADIATING FROM THE HEART EXPLORATION

In this exploration, you will radiate the sound of "O" from your heart into space. Notice the perceptual shifts as you distribute the sound beyond the membrane of your body, rather than containing the sound within your limbs as you did in the previous exploration. By slightly shifting your attention and intention, new and varied responses are able to emerge.

PHASE 1
-   Return to sounding "VUH" with your hands resting on your heart.
-   You could be lying down, as in the previous exploration, or you could be seated or standing.

PHASE 2
-   Sound "O" like the rays of the sun, from your heart outward in all directions. Each ray may be formed with one "O" sound, or it may take more than one "O" for the sound to travel fully from your heart.
-   After creating one stream of "O" into space, return to your heart to begin a new ray.
-   Send the rays in all 360 degrees around you from your heart into space.

PHASE 3
-   Lying on your back or side, curl your arms and legs in towards your heart. You could also begin curled over your legs, in what is known in yoga as "child's pose."
-   Explore radiating your heart's energy outward, opening your limbs and body with the "E" sound. Sense yourself as you relate to the energy all around you, near and far. Follow your natural inclination to determine when it is time to curl your body back inward.
-   Folding/unfolding, curling/unfurling and spreading/gathering are universal expressions of fluid movement in nature and in our bodies.

PHASE 4
-   Allow yourself to settle back into your baseline. Rest in open attentive awareness.

REFLECTION
What is similar or different in how you sense yourself now?
How did your experience in this exploration differ from the previous exploration, when you contained the sound within the limits of your limbs?

OPTIONAL PRACTICE CONTEXTS
The metabolic activity of digestion is another example of Fire in the human body. The two previous explorations can be adapted to radiate from the abdomen where the digestive organs are situated.

TENDERNESS OF HEART

I am not afraid of stepping
across the threshold
into the fire of the unknown
of sitting while the body pulsates
with undigested particles of this life
of staying while the system unwinds the knot.

It is the quality of attending I bring to these moments, I know less about.
The way of the heart
that knows only
of openness and infinite, silent gentleness.

THIS
ever-available suspension
around and in everything
inviting me
to simply

be here
with life
just as it is.

— PATRICIA BROWN

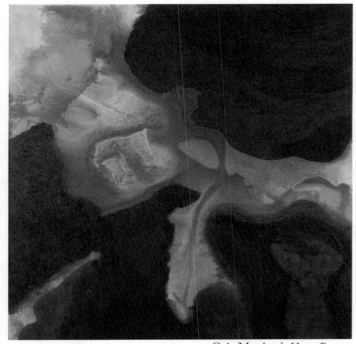

Gale Marsland, *Heart Passage*

The Spirit Soars, video, 10 min.

THE CREATIVE CAPACITY OF THE HEART

Fire is often associated with creative passion. When in a stream of creative flow, many artists speak of entering a state of unified consciousness by following the intuition of the heart.

Creativity often emerges as a response to meeting the unknown. As we learn to function in our social and cultural lives, we develop habitual patterns: in the movement of our thoughts, in the movement of our bodies and in our emotional responses. These patterns limit our perspective and narrow our options for development. Like Fire, creative engagement sometimes unfolds as instantaneous shifts and changes and other times as slow-burning ongoing adaptation. Creativity is a response to living. Emilie Conrad called creativity "the juice of life."

How do we cultivate the open, formless state from which creativity is birthed?

Fire Breath & Sounds,
demonstration video,
5 min.

THE BLURS

In a quest for a sound that could open a conduit to the undifferentiated territory of creativity, Emilie Conrad created the Blurs.

- A Blur is a short, low vocalization akin to a growl.
- Let each Blur have its own shape using your mouth and throat inventively with each sound.
- Leave different amounts of time in between sounds. In this way, each Blur is unique and emerges at unexpected intervals.
- While the Blurs originate from deep in your throat, it can be useful to engage your upper lip as if each Blur was passing through your upper teeth and maxilla (the bone that anchors your upper teeth).
- The guttural quality of the Blurs activates the front/gut body and the engagement of the upper lip awakens connection to the nasal passages, skull and back body.

The primal quality of the Blurs assists in shifting us away from the habits that anchor our day-to-day being and into a more-than-human state in which we can play with expression without judgment.

COSMIC BLUE
(EXCERPT)

A sound without shape, low,
closer to human
further from culture,
almost a vowel
but gone to the wild
before even the throat
can catch it.

— NOELLE ADAMO

OCTAVES
(EXCERPT)

I am not human all of the time
when my hips rock to the hips of others
unseen, when my most delicious growl
inspires a delicate turn of the head,
when I rest in the opportunity to move.
I release repetition, I regard impulse
and eyes closed,
I taste sugar in the stars.

— NOELLE ADAMO

SPARKING EXPLORATION – COURTING THE UNEXPECTED

The intention of this exploration is to stir you into a state of coherent disorientation. To be coherently disoriented is to view your environment from an unfamiliar vantage point, yet with enough structure to maintain a sense of support and grounding.

This exploration engages the quadruped position as both the impetus and support for disorientation. Moving on all fours brings us closer to the earth and into our animal bodies, moving us away from our biped consciousness and the habits it holds.

This exploration leads you to a blank place, a state of freshness. It is a particularly reinvigorating experience on days when you're feeling stuck, stymied, frustrated or unenthused.

Entering coherent disorientation can prepare you for any creative endeavor. It is a state of being with the messy generativity of ideas and impulses and of coexisting with loose ends that don't immediately resolve themselves. Coherent disorientation is a practice of being in process, navigating when you don't know where you're going and tolerating not knowing where you might end up. All of which is essential for creativity to blossom.

PHASE 1

- Sit with your hands resting somewhere on your body. Prepare yourself for bursts of energetic movement with a few rounds of the "LA" sound.
- When you feel like you have lit the flicker of your inner flame, move to Phase 2.

PHASE 2

In this phase, you will alternate between slow movement with the "sh…" breath and quick bursts of movement with the Blurs.

As you explore, limit yourself to positions in which your limbs are in contact with the ground, your body or another surface of support. Press and glide your limbs across these surfaces to change position, lifting a hand or foot only when no other movement is available in order to comfortably move through space.

By not allowing the release of energy through your limbs, you will make your experience more potent and find entirely new and novel ways to move your core body.

- Come to a quadruped position. Some options include: bearing weight on your hands and knees, on your hands and feet, or kneeling with your hands or forearms resting on the seat of a chair.
- Ride the "sh…" breath into slow fluid movement.
- Alternate slow motion "sh…" movement with short Blur bursts.
- Pair each Blur with a short, quick spurt of movement.
- Set an intention for the Blur - the sound itself - to be the impetus for each movement gesture. In this case, a movement gesture is a brief impulse, not a continuous phrase of movement.
- Encourage each Blur sound and movement spurt to emerge from a different place within your core body. Try your best not to preconceive what part of your body will become active, nor how it will move.
- After the Blur bursts, pause, reorient and return to the slow motion "sh…"
- You may find yourself shifting to a new quadruped position to·begin again.

Each Blur will take you to an unknown place. It is important to allow yourself time to register where you end up after each Blur. Pause in these potent spaces. You may feel as if you were mixed up in a blender. Allow time to investigate the process of reorienting yourself and begin your movement anew.

PHASE 3

- Begin in any position. Seated, standing or lying down.
- In this phase your limbs are no longer anchored in quadruped. Allow your limbs to move freely through space.
- Return to the alternating process of "sh…" breaths and Blur bursts from Phase 2.
- Let each Blur burst be a spark, a spontaneous gesture.

REFLECTION

Moving from new positions often brings new awareness. What did you discover from each round of this exploration?

What "sparked" in you during this exploration?

The Blur bursts can leave us in a disoriented state. How did you "find" yourself in these places?

What possibilities emerged for you?

What is possible if you apply your strategies of reorientation to other aspects of your life?

Barbara Mindell, *Earth Fever*

TEMPER ME

This cauldron
This burning
This fire
This longing of my life
Which burns me from the inside
Threatens to consume me

"Go to the limits of your longing"
The Poet enthralls me*
"Flare up like a flame"
"Embody me"

I'm cast into the furnace
To test my faith
The flame inside me rises
Greater, stronger, fiercer
Than the fire which surrounds

I breathe in the heat, the smoke
Feed the longing which I fear
Will annihilate me

There in those flames
In the shadows cast by
That great glaring light
Form takes shape
Emerges to stand beside me

The king and all watching eyes
Perceive in awe
No longer one alone
But two
The loved and the beloved
Reach, take each other's hand
Walk forward into life.

— RAINE BROWN

*RAINER MARIA RILKE: BOOK OF HOURS I 59

THE THREE ANATOMIES & FLUID ANATOMY

Emilie Conrad, founder of Continuum, with contributions from colleagues, formed the concept of the Three Anatomies: Cultural, Primordial and Cosmic. Each of these ways of being in the world has purpose. We inhabit them simultaneously, although not always equally, and one is not of greater value than the other.

We live our days in a body that performs tasks of survival and skill. The ability to shift from this Cultural Anatomy into relationship with your own unharnessed, liberated life force, in service to nothing other than its own expression, is one of the possible outcomes of Continuum exploration. Tapping into this vital potential is enlivening and available *free of charge* to everyone.

Along the way, encounters with the Primordial Anatomy, the aspects of our biology that echo the creatures of land and sea that evolved before humans, lay groundwork for an awareness of interconnection with all planetary life.

Throughout the explorations in this book, you may have the sense of being boundless, timeless and connected from the smallest particle of existence to the mysterious unknowable. In Continuum, these experiences are referred to as being in the Cosmic Anatomy.

The term Fluid Anatomy reflects the dynamic, phase shifting, holistic state invoked in Continuum practice. Allowing fluidity to pervade us changes how we relate to others and to nature. Being guided by our Fluid Anatomy is not only an antidote to the demands and impediments imposed by the Cultural Anatomy; it is also an evolutionary pathway towards living in a mutable manner, one in which we are adapting to life with fluid grace.

WATER

All living things
Root, spread and reach in all directions
and they thrive on the movement
and nourishment of water
— BOBBIE ELLIS

David Gilbert, *Flow 2*

How can becoming like Water reduce fragmentation and restore wholeness?

Our bodies are primarily composed of fluids. So many of our tissues are fundamentally liquid-filled cells afloat within biological seas. Our fluid nature reflects that of the earth. We are rivers of blood, pools of lymph and tides of cerebrospinal fluid. Our fluids are transformers, giving rise to life supporting processes, absorbing nutrients and dissolving toxic substances.

Lack of movement or the performance of repetitive actions can impede the flow of fluids within our bodies, causing us to feel stiff and tense. Intentionally moving like Water by drifting, flowing and meandering in waves, arcs and curves can unwind restrictions. We restore our innate fluidity which is mutable, adaptable and life-giving.

Water Dance, video, 8 min.

OBSERVING WATER, RESPONDING IN MOVEMENT

-   Visit a nearby water source. You could venture outdoors, locate Water within your home, or recall your experiences with a favorite watery place. You can also view videos of Water in natural environments or depictions of Water in art.
-   Use all of your senses to engage with Water. After a period of observing, mirror the movements of Water with your own body. You may crest like a wave, cascade like a waterfall, absorb like a wetland or pool like the water in the bathtub.
-   Explore moving like Water with your whole body or with one smaller section of you at a time. Move expansively in space or subtly within the membrane of your fluid self.
-   Gather clean drinking water from a local source. Hold a sip in your mouth, allowing the chemistry of the water to bathe your tongue. You deepen your relationship to place by taking in the Water of your environment.
-   Bathing the tongue stimulates the vagus nerve and cues the nervous system to settle. You may gently gargle the water before you swallow. The act of swallowing, allowing the water to integrate within you, may inspire movement response.

WATER MANDALA

After each exploration, let yourself be intuitively led to fill the circle of your mandala with color and shapes. Paint with watercolors or draw with pastel crayons.

When using pastel crayons, first apply the pastel. Then, after dipping your finger in a bit of water, rub and blend the pigment - activating the image.

You can create your own watercolor paints by combining plants and water from your environment with a few common household items.

CULTIVATING FLUIDITY

Your capacity for core body fluid motion and your breathing habits dynamically influence each other. The more variability in the movement of your breathing, the more mutable your internal volume becomes. Freedom of movement in your core body in turn allows for fuller, effortless breathing. You may experience a dissolving of your perception of boundaries, an expanded sense of self.

Often, we hold our torso in positions of stability by standing erect with a locked diaphragm, drawing our abdominals in and clenching our buttocks. This posture can be useful when needed, but if adopted continually can inhibit circulation, thereby impeding our vitality.

The natural movement of breath can be felt as follows.

- As you inhale, the diaphragm muscle spreads downward in the abdominal cavity. This action enlarges the space within the lungs and invites air to fill the negative space. You may notice a lifting and opening of your front body, particularly the breastbone, throat and face, and a gathering of hammock-like support in your back body.
- As you exhale, the diaphragm domes upward to fit within the concave bottoms of the lungs. The face falls gently forward in the gathering of the head and tail towards the fetal curve. You may notice a broad rounding of your back body and the soft hollowing of your front body. This cycle occurs ceaselessly and effortlessly within you. It is your own personal tidewaters ebbing and flowing.

THE WAVE MOTION OF BREATHING

Seated, with eyes closed or gaze softened, place your hands on your breastbone.
Notice the wave motion of your torso as you inhale and exhale.
Notice the upward rising, the cresting, of your breastbone as you inhale.
Notice the softening downward, the receding, of your breastbone as you exhale.
Gradually, allow more of your core body, from head to tail, to participate in the wave.
Allow each inhalation to encourage elasticity in your movement.
As your inhalation slips into exhalation and then returns again you are drawn to ripple elsewhere.
Ride these waves until they become quiet and you return to stillness.

Prue Jeffries, *Water & Light Venice 1*

MY BODY OF WATER
(EXCERPT)

Soul set in motion,
I dive into waters
larger than myself.
I too learn to swim.

— NOELLE ADAMO

Water Breath & Sounds,
demonstration video,
7 min.

DEEPENING CORE BODY WAVE MOTION WITH ZEPHYR BREATH

How can we rest into the ongoing, vital miracle of breathing?

As you fall into the natural movement of your breathing, you slow yourself down to notice the elaborate orchestration within you. You may become aware of sites and sensations of ease in your breathing and you may notice places of inactivity.

Many factors can inhibit breathing. Tightness in the jaw often leads to reduced activity of the diaphragm. Continuum teachers Linda Rabin and Elaine Colandrea developed the Zephyr Breath in their research to relax the soft tissue musculature of the jaw. Zephyr Breath is named after the mythological wind known as Zephyr in the painting by Botticelli, "The Birth of Venus."

- Inhale with softly closed lips. While exhaling, slowly blow air into your cheeks, allowing a small stream of breath to exit your mouth.
- As your cheeks billow with breath, the muscles of your jaw will relax.
- Encourage this release by gently sliding your jaw forward as you puff, like a sailboat gliding on water when the wind is in its sails.

Position yourself on your back with your head and legs comfortably supported.

- Rest your hands at your lower abdomen and gently breathe three Zephyr Breaths. Notice yourself filling and emptying, notice the waves of movement, however subtle, that may be occurring throughout your core body.
- Move your hands to your upper abdomen for three more breaths, allowing time for movement response.
- Continue moving your hands up your torso with the Zephyr Breath. Finish when your hands are at your collarbones, under which the upper lobes of your lungs extend on inhalation.

Often the first sensation of wave motion activated with breathing is a forward-back, head to tail ripple. Multidirectional flowing movement may also emerge. As always, ride the movement of your breathing, rather than forcing movement.

MY BODY OF WATER
(EXCERPT)

*My body of water
makes waves.
It knows calm
does not equal peace
and sometimes it must
rise and surge
in order to be heard.*

— NOELLE ADAMO

Prue Jeffries, *Water & Light Porto Venere 2*

Moving Like Water, video, 3 min.

INNER OCEAN EXPLORATION

*Can the wave motion of breathing awaken us to the fluids that bathe our cells,
as well as the fluids inside our cells?*

Within us is a watery realm akin to life's original home, the sea. As creatures, humans are part of an evolutionary arc from sea to land spanning billions of years. Much of the fluid within our bodies reflects the salinity of the marine world where the first life forms on earth began their journey.

The Inner Ocean exploration is a call to our primordial origins through the movement of the diaphragm, a wafting motion that resembles jellyfish propulsion.

The human diaphragm is a dome of soft tissue, a horizontal sheath dividing the chest from the abdomen. The downward movement of the diaphragm can be felt as the ribs expand outward on inhalation, like the surface of a trampoline being pulled taut. Upon exhalation, the diaphragm moves upward and the ribs softens inward, in a similar movement to the surface of a trampoline rebounding in slow motion. Jellyfish move by stretching and rebounding a ring of muscle around their bodies in a similar pattern.

As you explore the movement of the diaphragm, the jellyfish wafting within you generates multidirectional waves, which amplify your ability to sense yourself breathing globally, throughout your entire organism. Our bodies rely on the free flow of breath as one means to circulate fluids, promoting health by distributing nutrients and removing unneeded cellular byproducts.

PHASE 1
- Seated with your torso freely vertical, rest your hands receptively on the sides of your middle or lower ribs.
- Bring your attention to the movement of your breathing.
- Observe the continual flow of expansion and softening that occurs with each breath.
- Notice if there is a difference between the sides of your body.
- Notice if there are pauses after inhaling or exhaling.

PHASE 2
- Sound a low elongated "hum" while slowly drifting your rib cage from side to side. Repeat for approximately six cycles of breath. Your hands can remain on your ribs, or not, while you bathe in the "hum" vibrations.
- Suspend the "hum." Return your hands to your sides and observe the movement of your ribs once more. Note if there are any changes.

PHASE 3
- In this round, as you "hum," drift in diagonal movements from the midline of your body.
- Allow your exploration to grow to include upward and downward wafting movements, too.
- Continue with this multidirectional floating. Notice the spaces between your "hums," in which you are effortlessly propelled by the wave motion of your breath, your inner jellyfish. Letting go of effort, we yield to possibility.

PHASE 4
- Ride your breath and sound into more expansive movement. Perhaps the floating, drifting motion of your core body will spill outwards into wafting limbs, as if you are a creature of the sea suspended in water.
- In subsequent rounds, explore from other beginning positions: standing, on all fours and, lastly, from lying down.

REFLECTION
How do the motions of your diaphragm influence how you feel in your body?
What does multidirectional movement awaken in you?

Embryonic Origins with Continuum, video, 1 min.

LIFE FORCE EXPRESSION

Growth cannot occur in a static environment. The moving exchange of fluids is necessary for life to express itself. The universal growth motif of folding and unfolding is present in all of our movement throughout life, even in the fluids in which our very first cells were suspended.

During early development, the complexity of overlapping waves of fluids within an embryonic sac creates an enriched environment for cells to grow and divide.

The developmental sequence of an embryo, from a collection of cells to a recognizable body, shares similarities with the evolutionary phases of life on earth. In Continuum exploration, earlier stages of our own development - aquatic, amphibious and reptilian - may be invoked. An arm may be sensed as a wing or a leg as a fin, awakening us to mysterious primordial connections not often recognized in daily life.

SEA LIFE EXPLORATION

Living organisms exist in relationship to their environments. The internal environments of aquatic creatures like seaweed and octopus are similar to their external environments. The interaction between the movements of these life forms and the movement of the water around them makes fluidity their primary characteristic.

In this exploration, we discover fluidity in our limbs by moving like seaweed and tentacles, inviting multidirectional movement within our joints. The joints of our arms and legs are spaces where capsules of synovial fluid bathe our bones and soft tissue.

To prepare the fluid-filled joint spaces, return to the "J-Z" sound, which was introduced in the Earth chapter.

PHASE 1: SEAWEED ARM PREPARATION

- Sound approximately three rounds of "J-Z" while lightly pressing interlaced fingers together, stimulating the many joints within your fingers and hands.
- Sound another three rounds with each of your hands encircling the opposite wrist.
- Slide your hands up to wrap around opposite elbows for the next cycle of "J-Z."
- Move your hands up to opposite shoulders and sound another round of "J-Z."

PHASE 2: SEAWEED ARM MOVEMENT

- From the final preparation position, shape your throat as if you were going to sound "O." Instead, quietly exhale. Let the streaming quality of the "O" breath inspire multidirectional meandering movements within each of your shoulders. Encourage those qualities in the other joints of your arms: elbows, wrists and fingers.
- Enter a discovery interval of movement play where your arms take on the quality of seaweed in water.
- Your arms will likely separate from each other. Encourage each arm to follow its own unique, natural expression.
- When you feel complete, come to a position of rest.
- This seaweed arm movement play can be done seated, standing or lying down. In each layer of your exploration, begin in a different position.

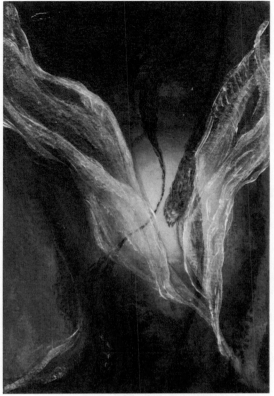

Barbara Mindell, *Ocean Depths Fluidity*

PHASE 3: TENTACLE LEG PREPARATION

Human legs spend a lot of time bearing weight and doing repetitive movements like walking. The joints are far apart and the bones are long. All of this makes finding fluidity within our legs more challenging.

- Begin this preparation from a seated position or while lying down on your back.
- Interlace the fingers of each hand between the toes of each foot. Direct the "J-Z" sound with light fingertip pressure into the vestigial "webbing" between each toe for three sounded exhalations.
- Slide each hand to encircle each ankle for three rounds of "J-Z."
- Continue up your legs until each hand is directing rounds of "J-Z" into the joint capsules of your knees.
- Following the long bones of your thighs, travel your hands to your hip joints, approaching from the inner thigh of each leg. Direct your "J-Z" sounded exhalation into this region.

PHASE 4: TENTACLE LEG MOVEMENT

For this part of the exploration, consider lying on your back with two soft 9-inch balls or two pillows under your hips, so that each half of your pelvis has its own support. This position decreases the feeling of density in your pelvis and encourages a sense of weightlessness in your legs. Your legs and feet are extensions of your pelvis. This position increases the sense of connection between your legs and hips.

- At the end of the Tentacle Leg Preparation, come to your back and raise your hips on two soft balls or two cushions. Bring your knees into your chest.
- Begin sounding "O." Let the sound stir the fluids in your toe, ankle, knee and hip joints. Slowly wander around within your joints, letting each joint have its own independent movement.

REFLECTION

What new information are you receiving from exploring with your limbs in this novel way? How does developing a sense of connection with other forms of life affect how you move in your body and in the world?

OPTIONAL PRACTICE CONTEXTS

The focus of this exploration is on arms and legs, but the same sequence can also be investigated along the midline of the body, bringing attention to the many joints in the spine, from tail to head.

LIKE WATER
(EXCERPT)

Our ancestral waters are on the inside
Each species calling us
Back to intelligent, fluid discovery

Opening time and space
To commune with our origins…

— BOBBIE ELLIS

Prue Jeffries, *Water & Light Venice 3*

FLUIDITY — WATER BLESSINGS FOR OUR TIME

Chaos begets
rigidity
for containment

Rigidity begets
chaos
for freedom

Beneath our skin
fluidity dances and ripples
for life in between

Fluidity rises
to the evocative coherence of Love

Track
the gentle ebb and swell

Become
the terrifying
curl of a monstrous wave

Breathe deep

Dive within
the boundaryless ocean of being

— JUDI BACHRACH

Tuan Pham, *Tsunami*

Water Blessing, video, 4 min.

Water Blessing Instructions, video, 7 min.

WATER BLESSING

Water, as a teacher, can dissolve what no longer serves us and can support the best in us to grow a more beautiful world. We, and the planet, are filled with the elemental mystery of Water. Water is buoyant - it carries and guides. Water is purifying - it cleanses and renews. The Water Blessing exploration invokes Water to lead us into creativity and communication - hallmark processes of life force.

Water Blessings can be performed outdoors near, or in, a body of water and indoors with a bowl of water. Before beginning the exploration, prepare an offering to honor the waters of your own being and the living waters of your environment. Your offering may be naturally occurring, like a flower, an object that you craft specifically to place in Water, or your own body itself.

This exploration can begin standing, seated or lying down. As you progress, change your relationship to gravity by exploring each of these levels and vary directions in your movement. In nature, the more Water changes its direction and level, the more impurities are filtered away. Like Water, as we explore moving from different positions, we stimulate new pathways of circulation to our muscles, organs and bones, inviting a renewed sense of vitality.

The practice of Open Attention begins and ends each cycle of the Water Blessing. Take time to quietly notice your inner landscape – your breathing and sensations, your sense of your whole self.

PHASE 1: VERTICAL GESTURE WITH "O" SOUND

The Vertical Gesture encourages presence in the moment and establishes a bodily connection from Air to Earth. This gesture also acknowledges the midline of the body - a place of central organization from which so many bodily systems originate.

- Wait for an impulse to raise one or both arms overhead.
- Gently curl your fingers in, making a loose fist.
- Slowly bring your arm down the midline of your body, while sounding one or more "O."
- Repeat this sound and gesture until you feel present in yourself. Each time, let your gesture emerge in a unique and individual way.

PHASE 2: HORIZONTAL GESTURE WITH "E" SOUND

The Horizontal Gesture establishes a connection to our environment. This gesture also acknowledges the growth of body-wide systems from the midline outward, returning us to the branching of our systems into communication and interdependence with the world beyond our skin.

- Place both hands anywhere along the midline of your body - perhaps at your heart, belly or eyes - open your arms, each to their own side while sounding "E."
- To encourage the lateralization of the "E" sound, draw the corners of your mouth outwards as you exhale. Tone in the middle to lower range.
- Experiment with gesturing from various locations along your midline to evoke different experiences.
- Let yourself be drawn to a new area to begin each layer of horizontal gesture.
- Repeat this sound and gesture until you feel connected to the world around you. You may open your eyes and take in your environment.

PHASE 3: WATER GESTURES WITH "HAH" BREATH

These water gestures are an opportunity to tap into the refreshing, cleansing, revitalizing qualities of Water.

- Whether you are in contact with an actual or imagined source of Water, use your hands to cup Water and anoint yourself with it.
- Accompany your water gestures with the "hah" breath. Inhale through your nose, then exhale with the breath of "hah." The "h" shape relaxes the tongue and flows into the "ah" shape, which releases the jaw.
- As you respond to your contact with Water, a source of creation and of solutions, repeat these gestures over and over, varying the places where your hands contact your body, varying your position and relationship to gravity.

PHASE 4: BECOMING WATER WITH "HUM"

As Emilie Conrad was fond of saying, "If you want to know about something, become like it."

-   Ride the expansion of your inhalation and the dissolving of your exhalation into fluid movement. Move in wave-like motions: undulate, arc, spiral and curve.
-   Breathe in through your nose and exhale "hum." The vibration of the "hum" transmits throughout the whole of you, though you may notice your felt sense of the "hum" more in some areas than others. The steady vibration of the "hum" can awaken fluid movement response.
-   Move in slow motion following your own internal impulses. Sense the response throughout your being. Encourage one movement to flow into another.
-   If you become disconnected from what you are doing or find yourself moving in familiar or known patterns, pause or suspend your movement.
-   As you suspend your externally visible movement, pay attention to and be guided from deeper movement impulses you may not have noticed before.

Phases 1-4 can be layered as many times as you wish.

David Gilbert, *Moving Stillness*

PHASE 5: BLESSING WATER WITH AN OFFERING

-   As the final gesture of the Water Blessing, place your offering into Water.

REFLECTION

Moving like Water is a way to enter into an unknown space of open inquiry.

-   *What does this experience reveal to you?*
-   *What qualities are you aware of as you move?*
-   *How is your body changing?*
-   *What ideas, senses and feelings are emerging as you become like Water?*

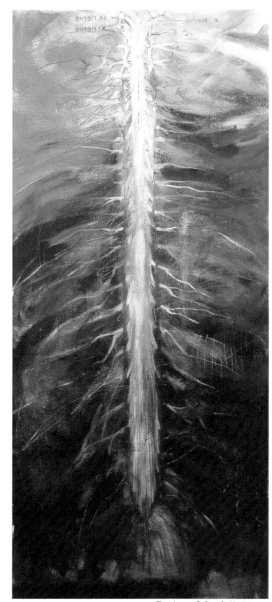

Barbara Mindell, *Nerve*

THE SEA WALKS

The ocean
crawled out onto a sunny shore
over millennia
breathtaking
walking within wondrous skin containers

Hold a body up
to an empty seashell
and listen

The brine of cerebrospinal fluid
continuously washes your brain
2,000 gallons of daily blood
gushes through your heart
lymph river systems hitch rides
surfing on your every move

Billions of neurons
communicate through chemical currents
molecular mermaids and mermen

silently partnering waves
overlapping
our internal body ballets

We flock back to the waters
as tourists on beaches
at rivers
lakes
ponds
pools, sinkholes and swamps
pay homage
to the sea of emergence

We never forget
the flux of our beginning
the ebb of our end
keep listening
for eternal tides
in every drop

— JUDI BACHRACH

SILENT NIGHT
(EXCERPT)

With each new awareness of beauty we are held
together in a communion of belonging.
When any one of us pauses to drink from the well of stunning glory
We are joined invisibly in our humanness.

— BETH PETTENGILL RILEY

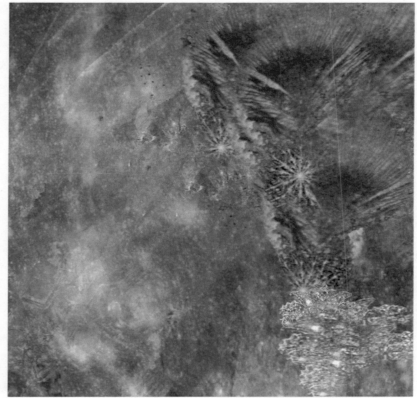

Shelley Ostroff, *Intimacy with the Infinite*

THE ALCHEMY OF
THE ELEMENTS

The whisper of enchantment and miraculous being,
As green urges upward – through rock and earth,
To pulsate with sun, air, rain and wind.
Simple magnificence.
— BETH PETTENGILL RILEY

David Gilbert, *Ground Found*

What are the processes involved in transformation?
What is your felt sense of innovation?

The preceding chapters have offered you direct interaction with the unique qualities and expressions of each element. As you refocus your sense of wonder to regard Air, Earth, Fire and Water in the whole of your relationship with the natural world, you will find the elements in constant interplay with one another. These intimate dynamics are the perceptible miracles of existence in life on earth.

Invisible Air creates visible forms in the bowing of windswept trees and the worn mesas of the high desert. Water wears away stone, creating canyons. The heat of Fire in the earth heaves upward, reshaping the landscape. Siltation of Earth fills in streams, changing the quality and direction of Water's flow. These are examples of the innovative processes involved in growth and evolution, both of a personal nature and on a universal scale.

In this chapter, you will move into a place of mystery, embodying the elements in their naturally entwined state. You, too, are an expression of this elemental fusion.

MAPPING EARTH, SCULPTING AIR

- Place yourself in a natural environment, although this exploration can also be done indoors.
- Begin by connecting your body with whatever surfaces are available.
- Moving in slow motion with the "VUH" sound (from Fire chapter), merge your body with the contours of your chosen landscape. Map the surfaces in an ever-shifting trail with every part of your body, feeling your form influenced by the form of your environment.
- Periodically, shift your attention. Bring in the "Sh..." breath (from Air chapter), letting your body carve the Air and space around you. Feel your form influencing the form of your environment.
- Continue to alternate *body mapping* the landscape with gestures that *sculpt space*. Notice the continuity of Air, Earth and you.

Ancestral Table, video, 4 min.

THE FIVE O'CLOCK CREEK
(EXCERPT)

And as the river sings back,
As the wind whistles through trees
And the light invokes galaxies inside my eyes
I am woven into this moment forever
And this moment is woven inside of me.

— BETH PETTENGILL RILEY

Four Element Fusion,
demonstration video,
12 min.

FOUR ELEMENT FUSION

In this exploration, you will begin by following an intentional elemental flow, from inner to outer, from rooting to soaring, experiencing contrast and harmony as coexisting parts of the same whole.

The phases of the exploration will be familiar to you from the prior chapters. Repetition and recombination provide endless opportunity for holism and nuance to coexist. *What might you notice now, which you did not previously?*

When you have completed one or more rounds in the order outlined below, allow yourself to layer the phases of the exploration without preplanned sequence. *What will you discover?*

Carol Woolgar, *Sensuous 9 (Lumini Merced)*

PHASE 1: IMMERSE IN WATER
- Begin seated in a chair or on the floor/ground.
- With the "Sh..." breath, follow meandering streams in the internal waterways of your core body. Encourage a sense of pouring from place to place within you.
- To activate the fluids in your core body, anchor your hands and feet to your body or the surfaces around of you.
- Subtly angle and shift your weight. As you pour in different directions, you are removing density from your tissues and unwinding your fascia. This pouring of your body increases circulation and nurtures organs, while stimulating the bones of the spine and pelvis.

PHASE 2: FLOW INTO EARTH
- With the vibratory sound "J-Z," press parts of yourself into the surfaces around you. Merge your body with Earth's body through shifting contact. Play with the degree of pressure in your contact from feather-light to full intensity.
- Press your palms into your legs, pelvis into chair and feet into floor. Eventually, come forward onto all fours.
- On all fours, press into the ground and feel the response of piezoelectric energy spreading upward from the earth through your body. The resistance of pressing stimulates bone growth and strengthens fascia, muscles and tendons.
- You may find yourself on your belly with a rolling, pressing movement coursing through you as you vary your points of contact with the earth.

Carol Woolgar, *Sensuous 3 (Lumini Merced)*

PHASE 3: WARM INTO FIRE

- Explore sounding "LA" like the flickering of a flame. Repeatedly sound "LA" on one continuous outbreath.
- Send the "LA" sound outward, radiating from your heart. Let the intensity of your beating heart unfold your limbs in a variety of pathways. Your limbs - arms, legs, head and tail - may extend singly, all together, or in combination.
- Enfolding follows unfolding, as your limbs return towards your heart.

PHASE 4: DISPERSE INTO AIR

- Enter into open movement with the "hah" breath.
- *Can you also let the Air around you, move you?* You may find yourself traveling from the floor to mid-level, standing and even moving through space, as well as returning to the ground.

PHASE 5

- Come to a resting place. Absorb what is unfolding within you. Observe your relationship with the world around you.

REFLECTION

What was revealed to you?

Did you notice any shifts in your perceptual habits as you layered these explorations of the elements?

Carol Woolgar, *Sensuous 7 (Lumini Merced)*

Carol Woolgar, *Sensuous 10 (Lumini Merced)*

Shelley Ostroff, *Spring*

AFTERNOON EMERGENCE

It's 4 pm and golden sunlight filters into the room,
bathing us divers in beauty.
The sun's very disappearance creates a light
unmatched by the day's dial.
As I drink in sparkling rays,
I ask myself if I would be so bold
as to willingly disappear every evening.
Would I rise up in the morning clear and totipotent,
freed from the sticky self of yesterday?
There's no standing still in the cycle of nature,
even when we refuse our own growth.
Fold and unfold, gather and sow.
Never stop dancing and you're on the way.
Your birth on the pilgrim's journey.
Our eyes shining like suns we greet each other in circle.
The portals are forever there,
offering resistance to invite our push.
Gather in — and the future can unfold.
We stand on generations, all woven into nature.
Will you step where you were meant to be,
where you can be seen,
so the world can go on,
more full, with you so clear?

— SANDRA CAPELLARO

RELATIONAL EMBODIMENT

KINSHIP WITH THE NATURAL WORLD

David Gilbert, *Planet Play*

How do we unite in kinship with the natural world?

Throughout your engagement with this guidebook you have practiced being in relationship with the elements. You have observed that what exists within you is also what comprises everything around you. Everything alive in your world is also what enlivens you. By cultivating a relationship with the elements you have practiced a continual remembering of your kinship with nature.

This relational embodiment is wholeness: listening with all senses open, curious and attentive. We partner with nature, learning its needs and negotiating our needs as well. Kinship with the natural world is one of the solutions to the passionate longing for connection that often arises in response to modern life.

How can we melt into the landscape, be there as observer, witness and lover, with a manner that is simultaneously focused and expanded? Being with the ephemeral expression of life in the present moment is an experience of wholeness encompassing the totality of creative and artful living. *Can we patiently enter such a realm with no agenda? What might unfold from such an exploration?*

What you direct, for yourself, in exploration will continue to emerge for you in life as an increased capacity for participation in the personal and collective challenges we all face.

My Body, The Wetland, video, 3 min.

In honor of the creative force residing in every person, we offer this final exploration.

EARTHBOUND, AIRBORNE

Lay on the earth or indoors in a comfortable pose.

Send "hah" breaths into the Earthscape below you.
Pause and be open to what you receive in return.

Send "hah" breaths into the Airscape above you.
Pause and be open to what you receive in return.

May you be inspired by the joy of continually unfolding into new domains of creative wellbeing.

Tuan Pham, *Dreamscape*

ABOUT WATERMARK ARTS

The Ways of Water, video, 2 min.

Watermark Arts brings together somatic awareness and artistic expression in the belief that both are essential aspects in creating a more humane and peaceful world.

The word somatic, from the Greek "somatikos," implies a fullness of presence in the living, sensate, wholeness of bodily being. With awareness of the integrity of the body, comes a felt experience of the interconnection of all living things as part of a larger whole.

In our modern, technologically-advanced era, somatic explorers exist near the cultural edge, holding this way of wholeness in the face of a widespread and pervasive sense of fragmentation.

Artists, too, live at the edge of culture, working with revolutionary ideas and symbolic messages encoded in dance, poetry, stories, music and visual art. As culture creators throughout history, artists have brought about substantive, peaceful change in society.

These times call on us to become generators of the culture we wish to live in. Creative acts show up in all aspects of life - in art, in teaching, in community-building. Watermark Arts asks, *What happens when these creative acts are informed by somatic awareness? Can we bring into being a world permeated by a sense of wholeness and interconnection?*

WWW.WATERMARKARTS.ORG

SUGGESTED READING

Abram, David. *The Spell of the Sensuous*. New York, NY: Random House, 1997.

Alexandersson, Olof. *Living Water: Viktor Schauberger and the Secrets of Natural Energy*. Bath, UK: Gateway Books, 1997.

Auchincloss, Priscilla Stanton and Beth Pettengill Riley. *A Moving Inquiry, The Art of Personal Practice*. Rhinebeck, NY: Epigraph Books, 2019.

Conrad, Emilie. *Life on Land: The Story of Continuum*. Berkeley, CA: North Atlantic Books, 2007.

Gintis, Bonnie. *Engaging the Movement of Life: Exploring Health and Embodiment through Osteopathy and Continuum*. Berkeley, CA: North Atlantic Books, 2007.

Jenny, Hans. *Cymatics*. New Market, NH: MACROmedia Publishing, 2001.

Marks, William E. *The Holy Order of Water*. Great Barrington, MA: Bell Pond Books, 2001.

Schwenk, Theodor. *Sensitive Chaos: The Creation of Flowing Forms in Water and Air*. Reprint, Forest Row, UK: Rudolph Steiner Press, 1999. First published 1965.

Zimmer, Carl. *At the Water's Edge: Fish with Fingers, Whales with Legs, and How Life Came to Shore but Then Went Back to Sea*. New York, NY: Simon & Schuster, 1998.

For more information on Continuum or to find a teacher near you visit:
www.continuumteachers.com

HELP & ONLINE SUPPORT

With questions or to access all digital content in one location, please visit:

www.watermarkarts.org/the-elemental-body-help-page

CALL FOR ART

We invite you to submit photos of your Elemental Mandalas to be included in a
community gallery on the Watermark Arts website.

- Please send each work of art as an e-mail attachment to: info@watermark-arts.org
- Use a file name that includes your last name and the title of your work (e.g. Colandrea _EarthMandala.jpg).
- Images should be sent as low resolution .jpg (ideally under 200KB).
- In the subject line of your email, include your name and "for Watermark Arts Mandala Gallery."

Thank you for your attention to these details!

ABOUT THE AUTHORS

Photo by Erik Kiviat

Elaine Colandrea's abiding interest in the transformative capacity of the body led to a master's degree in Dance Education from Columbia University and careers in dance/choreography, somatic education and bodywork. Authorized to teach Continuum by Emilie Conrad and Susan Harper, Elaine offers workshops from New York's Hudson Valley, teaches regularly in Italy and has been an invited presenter at Associazione CranioSacrale Italia, Dharmakaya Center for Wellbeing, ISMETA, Omega Institute and Shantigar Foundation.

   Elaine's deep passion for bringing together somatic practice and artistic expression guided the creation of Watermark Arts. As Artistic Director of Watermark Arts, Elaine curates digital art galleries; produces exhibitions, films and performances; publishes an annual journal and hosts conferences and workshops. The inquiry closest to her heart is how the somatic arts foster healthy relationships with oneself, others and the natural world.

www.elainecolandrea.com

Photo by Brian Colleran

Rori Smith is an artist, somatic movement educator and researcher of bodily experience. She holds a master's degree in Dance from Temple University and is currently a doctoral student in Dance & Philosophy at The University of Maine. Her work explores the nature of sensation, how our senses connect us with our environment and the ethics of this relationship. Rori has been immersed in Continuum since 2014, a practice that grounds her in the subtlety of each lived moment. In service to the somatic arts community, she writes and edits for Watermark Arts.

CPSIA information can be obtained
at www.ICGtesting.com
Printed in the USA
BVRC100857160622
639398BV00002B/1

9 781954 744745